FOSSIL BIRDS

Frontispiece. *Ichthyornis victor*. Restoration by Maurice Wilson.

British Museum (Natural History)

FOSSIL BIRDS

BY W. E. SWINTON
Senior Fellow of Massey College,
University of Toronto

Third Edition

Trustees of the British Museum (Natural History)
London 1975

First Edition 1958
Second Edition 1965
Third Edition, revised 1975

ISBN 0 565 05397 3
Publication No. 397

BMNH/41/10m/2/75
Printed in Great Britain by Burgess & Son (Abingdon) Ltd., Abingdon, Oxfordshire

Contents

1. Introduction

Though the geological history of the birds has been studied in various aspects, it is not familiar to that wide section of the public which is interested in living birds, nor is it scientifically well known as most of the fossil birds are of Pliocene-Pleistocene age and closely akin to the modern avifauna. The farther we look back in time the fewer the records become. In the Cretaceous, the number of kinds of birds known can perhaps be counted on the fingers of both hands, while in the earlier, Jurassic, period one finger will suffice for the purpose. Farther back than the middle of the Jurassic the geological record gives us no sign of the origin and development of birds, and all our clues are taken from peculiarities and similarities of the bones of certain kinds of reptiles.

The British Museum (Natural History) is fortunate in possessing many important specimens illustrating stages in this avian history, including, of course, the first skeleton to be found of *Archaeopteryx*, the oldest bird known. In addition, the Department of Palaeontology has a valuable and representative series of fossil birds from many parts of the world and an even fuller selection of reptilian remains such as is essential for comparative study.

The richness of this material is largely due to Richard Owen, Professor of Comparative Anatomy and Physiology at the Royal College of Surgeons, who was one of the pioneers in this line of research. Later, he became Superintendent of the Natural History Departments of the British Museum (then still in the parent building at Bloomsbury), and many valuable specimens came into the collections as a result of his interest.

The rarity of bird remains is largely due to their habits, for it must be assumed that, in the past as now, the majority of birds lived on land so the preservation of their remains was unlikely; their carcasses, like those of any land animal, lay unburied on the surface and were usually devoured by scavenging carnivores or destroyed by the usual processes of weathering. However, when birds died in the water, or were carried off by stream or wave-action after death, the skeletons were often buried in muds and silts, and the prospects

1

of preservation and fossilization were accordingly much greater. Naturally, there are great differences in the richness of deposits. The Middle Miocene freshwater limestone of Sansan in the Gers department of southern France has produced nearly 7000 specimens of fossil birds, yet the Lower Pliocene deposits of Pikermi in Greece, not dissimilar in formation from the beds of Sansan, have yielded only a few examples of four kinds of birds.

In spite of the patchiness of the evidence it is clear that birds are closely related to the reptiles. The older forms have many characters in their skeletons that suggest their derivation from that group; even living birds still show several peculiarities that can otherwise only be seen in long-extinct reptiles.

Before dealing with the extinct birds in detail, it will be advisable to indicate some of the principal features in the story of flight itself so that the reader may become familiar with both the problems involved and the structure of the creatures.

2. History of flight

The history of flight concerns not only the birds, for several classes of animals have attempted the conquest of the air and some have achieved notable success.

The earliest flying animals were the insects which attained great size and prominence in the Carboniferous period, when they may be said to have played the part now taken by the forest birds. Insects are, of course, true fliers, whereas many other animals that are said to fly are merely gliders. For example, among living animals, flying-fishes, flying-frogs, flying-snakes and lizards, flying-phalangers, flying-squirrels and flying-'lemurs' are all gliders of greater or less efficiency. In flying-fishes the pectoral fins are greatly enlarged, and when the fish is in flight they are held expanded at right angles to the body. The initial impulse to lift the fish clear of the water is, however, given by the tail. Flying-frogs have unusually long fingers and toes: when they jump from one tree branch to another they spread the digits, and the web between them, so that each limb ends in a small gliding surface.

There are flying-lizards (*Draco*) in Malaysia with lateral skin folds which when extended give a relatively large area for wing gliding. Unlike somewhat similar folds in the mammals, in *Draco* they are supported during the glide by extensions of the ribs. When not in use the 'wings' and their ribs are folded back and lie close to the animal's side.

A different mechanism is seen in the Indian flying-snake, which makes a parachute descent rather than a glide. When the snake is frightened it will fall from a branch, keeping the body rigid, with its ribs expanded and its belly muscles drawn in, so that a concave parachute extending most of the length of the body is formed thus enabling the reptile to descend safely to the ground.

Among mammals the so-called flying-foxes of the tropics are in fact fruit-eating bats. The flying-'lemur' or Colugo of the East Indies, a tree-living herbivore the size of a squirrel, is not a lemur and glides rather than flies. Its mechanism is simple, for the Colugo (*Galeopithecus*) has a fold of skin on each side of the body that stretches from the neck to the tail and includes the hands and feet. These folds when extended form wings that enable glides of up to 60 metres to be made.

All these are modern forms of flying animals and, apart from the insects, none has any considerable geological antiquity. Among the higher vertebrates or back-boned animals the oldest are undoubtedly the Pterosauria, flying reptiles commonly called 'Pterodactyls', although this name properly refers to one group. They are first found in the lowest limits of the Jurassic. Pterosaurs are of two main kinds, the long-tailed Rhamphorhynchoids and the short-tailed or true Pterodactyls. The former were confined to the Jurassic and may be exemplified by *Dimorphodon* of the English Lower Lias and by *Rhamphorhynchus* itself from the Jurassic of Germany.

The true Pterodactyls were undoubtedly derived from the Rhamphorhynchoids. Beautiful skeletons of the typical form *Pterodactylus* have been found in the Kimmeridgian of Solnhofen in Germany and fragmentary specimens of the much larger *Ornithocheirus* occur in the Cambridge Greensand and Chalk of England. To this latter group also belongs the great *Pteranodon*, represented by almost complete skeletons from the Niobrara Chalk of Kansas, U.S.A. Some members of this genus had a wing span of over 8 metres and are the largest flying animals known. The pterosaurs pass completely from the geological record towards the end of the Cretaceous, being replaced by the birds which had first appeared in the Upper Jurassic. Thus for nearly a hundred million years pterosaurs and birds had flown together in the Mesozoic skies.

Bats, more closely similar to the flying reptiles, in mechanism if not in habits and range, were comparative late-comers. The earliest known fossil forms with well-developed wings are some fifty-five million years old and come from the Middle Eocene strata of both Europe and North America. Soon after this many forms of bats appear to have been well established.

Vertebrate animals have thus attempted true flight three times, and each attempt has been successful – even if pterosaurs did eventually become extinct. Each of these successes was separately achieved: pterosaurs did not evolve into birds – nor did the birds give rise to the bats.

3. How birds fly

The methods used by animals to sustain themselves in the air are very varied. The body skin flap at its simplest is easy to understand, and this gradually develops into a patagium or skin wing, as in pterosaurs and the bats. This process however, (see Fig. 1), gives no clue to the development of the true wing of birds.

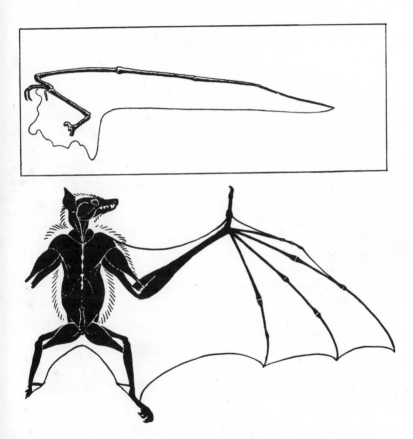

Fig. 1. Wings of pterodactyl (above) and bat (below) for comparison with bird wing. Lower drawing by Maurice Wilson.

We shall see shortly how the first birds appear to have arisen from reptilian ancestors, but the transition from reptilian scales to the quite differently constituted and arranged feathers of the bird is still a mystery. The wing has many advantages over the more vulnerable and weaker web of skin of the pterosaur or even of the bat.

The pterosaur wing appears to have been efficient for many millions of years, yet it is obvious that injury to the slender outer end of the wing finger would be very easy to sustain on nearing the water and when this accident occurred the delicate membrane would tear like a piece of paper. The bat's wing has a very similar skin covering but this is rendered less vulnerable and is kept in shorter sections by the different arrangement of the supporting bones. There is a framework here that supports the patagium and does not merely supply a leading edge. Rupture of the membrane is much less likely in a bat and if it does occur the damage is restricted.

The wing of the bird is formed of a series of feathers with supporting skeleton and has a bony leading edge just as efficient as that of the stoutest pterodactyl. The feathers together form a structure and surface that are mechanically more efficient that those of either flying reptile or mammal. If mishap occurs, apart from an incapacitating accident to the supporting limb bone, probably only a feather or two is involved and the resulting gap can be covered temporarily by rearrangement of the other feathers, until the new feathers replace the old after the next moult. (Figs. 2 and 3).

The method of coverage of the feathers is very economical and a brief description of it is essential if an understanding of bird flight is to be made for comparison with the conditions in the earliest known birds.

The feather (Fig. 4) itself consists of a main stem (scapus), divided into a hollow tube-like portion, the quill (calamus), and the solid squarish shaft (rachis) beyond. The last has a number of processes or barbs attached to it, and from them in turn are developed barbules that interlock and thus help to make the firm and elastic vane of the feather.

There are, however, several kinds of feathers. Pennae or contour feathers, like that outlined above, are of two main kinds: quills and coverts. The quills form the large feathers of the wing and the tail where they are known respectively as the wing quills or remiges

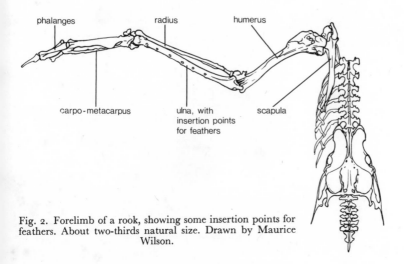

Fig. 2. Forelimb of a rook, showing some insertion points for feathers. About two-thirds natural size. Drawn by Maurice Wilson.

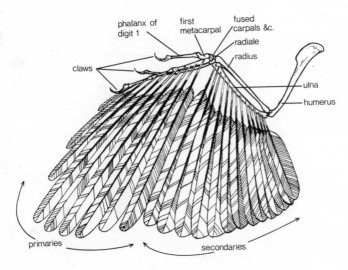

Fig. 3. The feathered wing (restored) of *Archaeopteryx lithographica* seen from above. Even in the earliest bird a satisfactory wing of nine primaries and fourteen secondaries existed. Note the claws in *Archaeopteryx* as compared with the modern bird in Fig. 2. About half natural size. Drawn by Maurice Wilson.

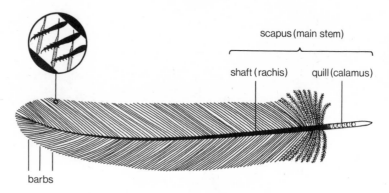

scapus (main stem)

shaft (rachis)   quill (calamus)

barbs

Fig. 4. Contour feather of a domestic fowl (*Gallus*), showing the calamus and rachis, and (enlarged) the interlocking mechanism between adjacent barbs by means of minute barbules.

(rowing feathers) and the tail quills or rectrices (steering feathers). It should be noted that the word 'quill' has two uses: for a part of the feather and, more commonly, as here, for a large feather of the wing or tail.

Wing quills are of three different kinds: the primaries, attached to the bones of the hand (manus), and which have the posterior part of the vane broader than the anterior; the secondaries or cubitals attached to the ulna, and which are generally shorter than the primaries; and thirdly, the humerals borne on the anterior half of the humerus (Figs. 2, 5). In addition to these there are three quill feathers attached to the thumb and forming the 'bastard wing' (alula).

The coverts are short feathers that cover parts of the remiges and rectrices and give them additional rigidity and which help generally to clothe the bird's body. It can be said that the barbules of coverts are less firmly interlocked.

The plumage or feather pattern of the wing gives an idea of the flying efficiency of the structure. The firm forward edge and the strong yet flexible wing acting on the air as a powerful lever when it is flapped cause air currents to be deflected backwards and downwards as the arched (and ventrally concave) wing moves forward. In general terms it may be stated that the primaries are responsible for the propulsion and steering and the secondaries are largely in

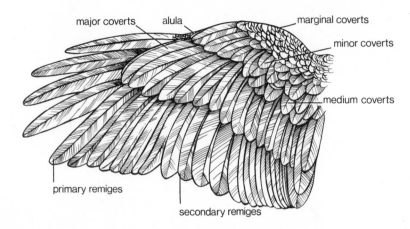

Fig. 5. Extended wing of a sparrowhawk (*Accipiter*) from above, showing the distribution of the remiges and coverts. Compare Fig. 2: the primary remiges are attached to the manus, the secondaries to the ulna.

control of the lifting movement. The thumb-feathers (or bastard wing) may be used in preventing the bird stalling.

The wing is perfectly efficient for maintaining gliding flight, as the habits of the albatross amply prove, but its value is materially increased in muscular flight by the development of powerful muscles for raising and lowering the arms, causing the wings to beat the air. One has only to see the skeleton of a duck in the flying position to appreciate the very considerable lifting power of the wings.

The muscles themselves seriously affect the processes but there is a ready method for the estimation of their ability. Any muscle is powerful only in so far as it has an effective leverage and a suitable base for its origin and insertion. The trunk vertebrae and the shoulder and pelvic girdles of flying birds all show adaptations for this muscular purpose. (See Fig. 6.) The thoracic vertebrae of the duck, for example, are seven in number and of these the first five are firmly united by their neural spines and the two hinder vertebrae have their centra fused with the lumbar vertebrae. As a series the vertebrae thus form an unusually strong muscular basis. The additional lift derived from this mechanical process also depends on other factors, such as the density of the air, the speed of the wind, the area of the

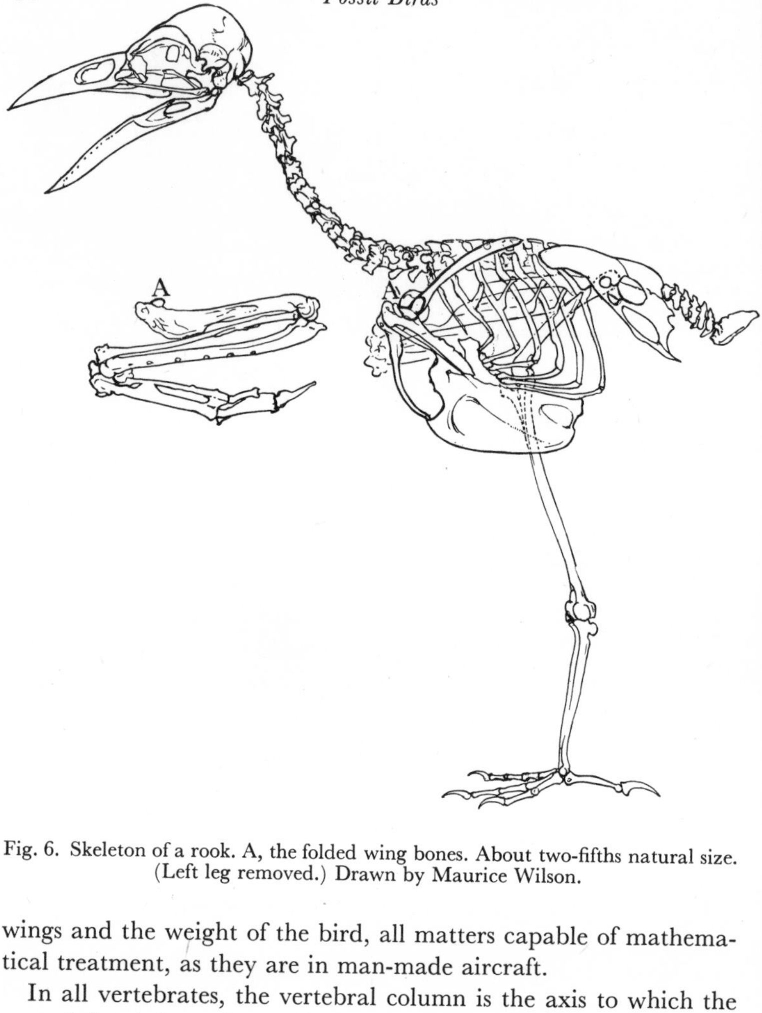

Fig. 6. Skeleton of a rook. A, the folded wing bones. About two-fifths natural size. (Left leg removed.) Drawn by Maurice Wilson.

wings and the weight of the bird, all matters capable of mathematical treatment, as they are in man-made aircraft.

In all vertebrates, the vertebral column is the axis to which the rest of the skeleton is attached in differing ways. The number of vertebrae so used varies from thirty-nine in certain small birds to sixty-three in the swan. In large part these higher numbers are due to the very long neck which is well shown by swans and herons, or in the domestic fowl after plucking. Whereas in mammals the number of neck vertebrae is almost always seven, in birds the number varies between eight (some humming-birds) and twenty-five (swan). All bird vertebrae have saddle-shaped articular surfaces giving them great mobility, but the cervical vertebrae are so well provided with processes for the attachment of muscles and ligaments, as well as with secondary articulations with their neighbours, that they are the most complex bones in the whole column.

The thoracic vertebrae are held firmly together by very strong ligaments to provide rigid support for the muscles of flight and as many as five of them may be fused together. When this happens, two or three free vertebrae are usually interposed between the fused bones and the sacrum. In this way the necessary flexibility of the back between the wings and the legs is assured.

The sacrum, which has to absorb the shocks of a comparatively heavy body alighting after flight, consists of from ten to twenty-three vertebrae fused together. The exact number varies slightly in any one species; in domestic pigeons it is twelve or thirteen, in the fowl thirteen or fourteen and in the wild duck seventeen. To this rigid structure the very large pelvis is attached. Lastly there are the caudal vertebrae, the first two or three of which allow free movement of the tail, whereas the remainder are fused into a single mass, the so-called ploughshare bone (pygostyle), which gives solid support for the tail quills. (See Fig. 23.)

The breast-bone (sternum) (Fig. 6) is the foundation on which the shoulder-girdle and the wing bones depend for their stability. It is the most easily recognized and certainly the biggest bone in the whole skeleton. It is a large curved plate of bone, broad in front and pointed behind, that forms the greater part of the ventral surface, the inside being concave to accommodate the lungs. Along the centre line of its ventral surface is a bony keel known technically as the carina; this is present in all birds except the kiwis and the ostriches and their allies (the Ratites), and from it the greatest primary division of the Carinates takes its name.

At each side of its front edge, the breast-bone bears the long and stout coracoid whose function is to transmit the strain from the wing to the breast-bone. The coracoids also serve as spacing bars in keeping the wings at the proper distance above the centre of gravity of the body and, together with the shoulder-blades (scapulae), share in forming the articular cavities for the humerus and wings.

The shoulder-blades are long, narrow and curved like scimitars. They pass backwards over the ribs on either side of the backbone and are firmly attached to them by strong muscles. The wish-bone, or 'merry-thought', is made by the fused clavicles or collar bones, two rods of bone with flattened ends; it lies immediately in front of the breast-bone and coracoids and is joined to them by ligaments.

To the rigid bony scaffolding formed by these different shoulder and breast elements are attached the flight muscles that move the wings. On each side of the keel of the breast-bone two muscles far exceed the others in importance and size. The larger muscle, the pectoralis major, lies immediately underneath the skin of the breast. It is attached to the whole of the outer part of the keel and of the breast-bone proper leaving a relatively small pocket, open in front, in which the smaller muscle is situated. It ends in a stout ligament that is fastened to the humerus; its function is to lower the wing on the down beat against the resistance of the air, and is usually large and powerful. The smaller muscle, the pectoralis minor, is not so powerful. It ends in a longer, thinner, ligament that passes up between the coracoid, scapula and wish-bone to be fastened to the humerus so that it works against the pectoralis major and raises the wing.

The hip-girdle is even stronger than the shoulder-girdle. Not only is it fused immovably with the sacral vertebrae, but it is also fused with the lumbar vertebrae, as well as with some of the anterior bones of the tail. The total number of vertebrae affected in this way varies, as stated, from ten to twenty-three according to the species; there are three hip-bones on each side, the two main bones, the ilium at the front of the leg and the ischium behind it, being greatly expanded with a concave outer surface. To them are attached the powerful muscles of the hind-limb.

This rigid and powerful structure is essential, for the hind-limbs are a bird's only means of moving when it is not flying; thus, they serve for hopping, running or swimming, as the case may be. Moreover, they furnish the initial impulse when a bird jumps upwards at the beginning of a flight and receive the initial shock when it lands.

Strength and rigidity are, however, only two of the most important requirements of the framework of a successful flying machine. A third character of equal importance is lightness. In aeroplanes this is

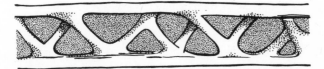

Fig. 7. Interior of a typical pneumatic bird bone showing the structure with internal strutting, which combines lightness and strength.

achieved by using light metals and in birds by reducing the amount of bony tissue to the absolute minimum. Bird bones (Fig. 7) are remarkable for the extreme thinness of their walls in comparison with their great mechanical strength. But this is not all: the cavities that in most animals are filled with marrow are in most birds occupied by delicate membraneous sacs filled with air; i.e. the bones are pneumatic. Thus the weight of the marrow is saved and, because the air-sacs are outgrowths from the breathing apparatus, the bird carries within itself reserves of air that play a vital part in the physiology of flight.

The oldest known bird, *Archaeopteryx*, is an exception to this general rule, for its bones have the normal reptilian structure. On the other hand, the pterosaurs had fragile hollow bones similar to those of birds, and show, therefore, that this character has been evolved independently at least twice, since the birds and the pterosaurs are not directly related. How extensive this system of air-sacs can be in birds is well exemplified by the albatross, in which every bone in the skeleton, apart from the shoulder-blades and the hyoid apparatus, is pneumatic.

The development of the power of flight has made severe and unusual demands on the physiology of birds, and, although the changes in anatomy that have taken place in response to those demands are mainly reflected in organs that are not preserved in fossils, they are so interesting that some reference to them must be made.

The efficiency of any animal, considered as a machine, is largely dependent on the arrangements made for supplying the blood with oxygen and for ridding the body of carbon dioxide. These arrangements concern the heart, the blood, the lungs, and the temperature of the body.

The heart is the pump that causes the blood to circulate through the body. Its size depends principally on the body weight of the bird and its evolutionary position. Small birds live a more active life than big ones and have a relatively larger heart. Similarly the more primitive birds have relatively smaller hearts than the more advanced ones. The second point may be illustrated by the raven and the pheasant, both of them of the same average weight – about 1·2 kg (approx. 2½ lb). The former, a member of the most advanced order, the Passeriformes, has a heart that averages 10 per cent of the body weight, whereas in the latter, a member of the somewhat primitive Galliformes, the heart is only about 5 per cent of the body weight. That the smaller birds have the relatively larger heart is shown by comparing a raven and a sparrow, which both belong to the Passeriformes, but whereas the raven's heart is about 10 per cent of the body weight that of the sparrow is 13·9 per cent. Hummingbirds, which probably have an average weight of 5 grams, have hearts that vary between 19·8 and 22 per cent of their body weight. Similar differences are found in the rate at which the heart beats, thus the rate in the turkey is 93 a minute whereas in the much smaller domestic fowl it is 312. Both these birds belong to the Galliformes and are approximately at the same level of organization. The sparrow, on the other hand, is much smaller and more highly organized, with a rate of 460 beats a minute.

Even the character of the blood changes with the size of the bird and its degree of organization. Thus, a peacock weighing 4·5 kg (10 lb) has about 2 700 000 red corpuscles in each cubic millimetre of blood, whereas a pheasant weighing 1·2 kg (2½ lb) has 4 800 000. By contrast, a blackbird, one of the more highly evolved group Passeriformes, weighs about 85 g (approx. 3 oz); its blood contains about 6 400 000 red corpuscles per cubic millimetre. The number of red corpuscles is only one of the factors in the efficiency of the blood as a carrier of oxygen to the different body-tissues, and as a means of ridding the body of the carbon dioxide formed through the vital processes.

A bird's lungs are peculiar among those of air-breathing vertebrates in that they play a secondary part in respiration, the more important part being played by the air-sacs. The lungs proper are closely applied to the backbone and adjacent parts of the ribs. The wind-pipe divides into two branches, one for each lung, which then subdivide many times within the lungs to form a tree-like arrangement of branches and twigs, but whereas in the mammals the twigs have blind endings, in the birds they are intercommunicating to allow the air to circulate freely.

The air-sacs lead off from the larger branches of the windpipe. They take the place of the marrow in the bones and also fill in the spaces between the convolutions of the intestines. When a bird is more or less inactive the air-sacs contain a large proportion of carbon dioxide and water vapour, but when it is actively moving these gases are expelled and replaced by fresh air.

The bird works its breast and belly against the backbone by muscular action, the motion being facilitated by a kind of hinge about halfway along the length of each rib. In this way the lungs and air-sacs are alternately compressed and expanded and the whole apparatus works like a pair of bellows. This system with its stress on expiration rather than inspiration is peculiar to birds and is remarkably efficient.

As a result of these adaptations many birds, like geese and starlings, can maintain an average speed of 80 km/h (50 m/h) in normal flight and exceed this considerably for short periods. The beating rate of wings varies enormously but some of the smaller species of humming-birds beat their wings 3000 times a minute.

It is clear that the whole anatomy and physiology of birds are derived from reptilian ancestors but have been great modified towards one end only, namely efficiency in the air.

4. Jurassic birds

In 1824 Dr W. Buckland made the first scientific description of dinosaur remains. These were bones of an animal that he named *Megalosaurus* and they came from the Stonesfield Slate at Stonesfield, which is not far from Woodstock and about 14·5 km (9 miles) north-north-west of Oxford. The fact is important, for these reptilian bones were said to have been accompanied in that deposit by bones of long-legged birds allied to the order Grallae (Gruiformes) 'thus affording the most ancient example yet discovered of the occurrence of birds'. Unfortunately the bones have since proved to be those of pterosaurs. For the origin of avian geological history one has to go to a point later in the Jurassic sequence and to discoveries made nearly forty years after Buckland's false start.

At Solnhofen in Bavaria there are great deposits of fine-grained limestone that have been laid down in a shallow sea or lagoon, in Upper Jurassic (Middle Kimmeridgian) times. The limestone is of such a fine and even grain that it has been extensively quarried and used for lithographic printing purposes, so much so that the beds are known as the Lithographic Limestone. During the course of working this stone it was natural that every piece should be examined with thoroughness and thus fossils and their imprints were frequently discovered as a by-product of the industry. In the course of years a very large series of fossils was amassed, including plants, invertebrates, fishes and reptiles, especially pterodactyls.

Dr Friederich Karl Häberlein, the Medical Officer of the district of Pappenheim, was interested in fossils and either visited some of the quarries or was frequently consulted by the quarry-men about their finds, many of which the doctor acquired for his own collection in payment for medical services. It was early in 1861 that the long and familier chain of fossil discoveries was interrupted by a quite new find, the imprint of an undoubted feather of a bird. There could be no doubt at all as to the reality of this isolated specimen, 68 mm long, with a vane 11 mm wide, and with rachis, barbs and barbules clearly shown. The fossil was found on one slab and there was an impression of it on the counterpart. The main slab went to

16

PLATE I. *Archaeopteryx lithographica.* Original, now in the British Museum (Natural History), London, from the Solnhofen Limestone, Bavaria. $\times \frac{1}{2}$

the Museum of the Academy of Sciences in Munich while the counterpart went to the Natural History Museum in Berlin; both specimens are still preserved in these institutions.

Quite soon after the discovery of this feather, also in 1861, at Langenaltheimer Haardt, near Pappenheim, Bavaria, in the Ottmann

PLATE 2. *Archaeopteryx lithographica*, the oldest known bird. Restoration by Maurice Wilson.

Quarry, a skeleton was discovered, also on a split slab, which was very like that of a reptile, but with the clearly marked imprint of feathers attached to the forearm, and of a long reptilian tail with many vertebrae, most of the vertebrae having a pair of short feathers appended.

The discovery caused a sensation amongst the workmen who, though very familiar with a wide range of fossils, had never seen anything like this before. The specimen passed almost at once into the hands of Dr Häberlein and its fame spread throughout Europe. Quite soon it was named *Archaeopteryx lithographica* by Hermann von Meyer, who recognized that the first-found feather belonged to the same kind of animal and must share the same name (Plates 1, 2 and 3).

By February 1862 the Keeper of the Geological Department of the British Museum was in correspondence with Dr Häberlein with a view to the purchase of the specimen. After much negotiation the 'feathered fossil', with 1700 other fine specimens from Dr Häberlein's collection, was bought for a total of £700 and arrived 'quite uninjured' at the Museum on 1st October, 1862. The sum paid to Dr Häberlein was given by him to his daughter for a dowry. Before coming to the Museum the fossil had been described (November 1861) by Professor Andreas Wagner as a long-tailed pterodactyl and given the name *Griphosaurus*. Professor Wagner had not seen the specimen and his opinion was based on hearsay.

Once in the Museum the specimen was subjected to a careful analysis of its characters and was fully described by Richard Owen in a number of papers under the new specific name of *Archaeopteryx macrura*.

Over a century has passed since the discovery of this fossil bird and it has been examined by many scientists who have reached different conclusions as to its place in the evolution of the birds. Two things are certain; it is a bird, but closely linked in its main characters with the reptiles.*

In 1877, at Blumenberg near Eichstätt, about 16 km away from the site of the original discovery, another and rather more complete

---

* *See* DE BEER, G. R., 1954. *Archaeopteryx lithographica.* 68 pp., 15 pl. British Museum (Natural History). In this work are gathered the fruits of many researches both old and new and the characters which give *Archaeopteryx* its unique place in the ancestry of birds are concisely summarized.

PLATE 3. *Archaeopteryx lithographica*, reconstruction.

Fig. 8. *Archaeopteryx lithographica*. Reconstruction of the skeleton. About one-third natural size. (After Heilmann.)

skeleton was found in J. Durr's quarry. This came into the possession of Dr Ernst Häberlein, son of Dr F. K. Häberlein who had the previous specimen, and was bought for £1000 on behalf of the Museum für Naturkunde, Berlin, where it came into the company of the counterpart of the feather found sixteen years previously. This specimen was later named *Archaeopteryx siemensi*.

This Berlin specimen, probably on account of its completeness, has not been subjected to the same degree of scrutiny as that in London. The latter (Plate 1) has been studied quantitatively and qualitatively, by direct and indirect lighting, by ultra-violet rays and X-rays. The preparators of the Palaeontological Department have pared away the limestone until every possible element has been revealed so that now it does, in fact, give information of the highest order of importance.

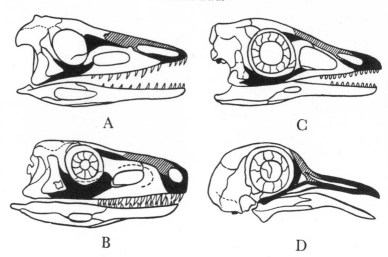

Fig. 9. Reptile and bird skulls compared. A, *Aëtosaurus ferratus*, Trias of Germany. B, *Euparkeria capensis*, Trias of Africa. Both are pseudosuchian reptiles. C, *Archaeopteryx lithographica*, Upper Jurassic of Germany. D, *Columba livia*, domestic pigeon, Recent. The dark areas are the premaxilla, lacrimal and jugal; diagonally shaded, the nasals. (Modified from Heilmann.)

It seems probable that our specimen of *Archaeopteryx*, a land bird of limited flying powers, was blown away in a gale and drowned in the nearby Solnhofen Lake. It lay under water imprinting its feathers on the underlying mud and to a lesser extent on the mud being gently deposited over it, the body meantime undergoing quite natural decay, so that although parts became disarticulated they did not become scattered. Only the lower jaw, the right foot, and some of the neck vertebrae are missing.

The following account is, however, based on both London and Berlin specimens. The bird was about the size of a raven, with a compactly built skull, in which rather reptilian characters can be seen (Fig. 8). There are, for example, large preorbital, narial and temporal fossae (see Figs. 9 and 10) and a post-temporal bar separating orbit and temporal fossa. There are short and rather cylindrical teeth in both upper and lower jaws, and the mandible has a fenestra like many fossil reptiles, as shown by the Berlin specimen which has both upper and lower jaws.

The orbit is large and has a complete ring of sclerotic plates. In

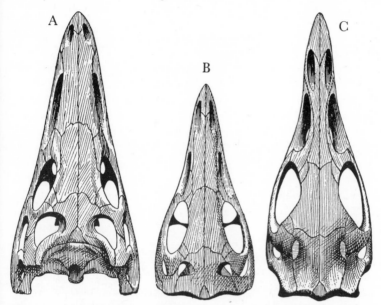

Fig. 10. Upper surfaces of the skulls of A, *Euparkeria capensis*; B, *Columba livia*; and C, *Archaeopteryx lithographica*. (After Heilmann.)

general appearance the skull is intermediate between that of pseudo-suchian reptiles such as *Euparkeria* and that of flying birds like *Columba*, the pigeon (see Fig. 9, D). The brain, which can now be largely reconstructed through the efforts of Dr Tilly Edinger of Harvard Museum of Comparative Zoology and of Sir Gavin de Beer, was undoubtedly similar to that of reptiles in both shape and structure and was different from that of all other known birds.

The vertebrae are certainly reptilian in structure for they are flat or very slightly biconcave on their articular ends and nowhere exhibit the saddle-shaped articulations found in other birds whether fossil or Recent. The total number of vertebrae in the neck is not completely known from either specimen but there are certainly ten, including the atlas; the trunk vertebrae are easily distinguished and appear to be twelve in number. There are eight sacrals and certainly twenty caudals. The caudals form one of the most interesting features of this primitive bird, for they are quite reptilian and arranged in a long chain unlike those of any other kind of bird.

In addition to the ribs normally borne by the vertebrae, there is a series of thin abdominal ribs or gastralia, which are not comparable in origin with true vertebral ribs.

The pectoral girdle is well preserved and shows the coracoid only one-third as long as the scapula. In modern birds of powerful flight the relationship is much closer than this (five-sixths in the duck), so that it can be deduced with some confidence that the pectoral muscles must have been short and the power of flight correspondingly poor.

The cup-shaped joint between the coracoid and the scapula also houses the end of the clavicle, whose other end is joined distally to its fellow, the whole structure being known as the furcula (Latin for a 'forked prop') but more familiarly and generally called the 'merry-thought' or 'wish-bone', an avian feature well developed in *Archaeopteryx*.

An important part of the pectoral girdle, lying in front and connecting the distal ends of the coracoids, is the sternum, a broad and short bone in *Archaeopteryx*, but a much longer and externally convex and keeled bone in most birds (see Fig. 6). Its plain and only slightly bowed ventral surface in the London specimen emphasizes what the shortness of the coracoid has already indicated, that this first-known bird was but a feeble flyer. Attempts have been made to contrast the conditions as found here with that of the Berlin specimen, which is alleged to have a keel but for which the evidence is conflicting. None the less, on wholly unconvincing evidence, the suggestion has been made that all flying birds or Carinates are derived from the Berlin specimen (differentiated because of this and other suggestions as *Archaeornis*) and all the non-flying forms, or Ratites, from the London fossil. It would be a remarkable coincidence if it were true.

The forelimb of *Archaeopteryx* is unusual in being as long as the hindlimb, a feature that must be of evolutionary significance. The bones were not very strongly developed. The humerus is longer than the radius and the ulna, all of which are well preserved, but the hand is poorly represented and recourse must be had to the Berlin specimen for information. From the combined evidence it is clear that the hand had three complete fingers, with strong, curved claws with horny sheaths.

The pelvic girdle has an elongated, rather dinosaurian ilium which forms, as in other birds, the major part of the acetabulum. The pubis, which meets its opposite fellow distally, forms a forked structure not unlike that of some Ornithischian dinosaurs, though the similarities here are probably the result of convergence rather than of relationship. The hind bone of the triad, the ischium, is peculiarly shaped and was probably completed by cartilage during life. As a result of the recent study, the pelvic girdles of the London and the Berlin specimens are now known to be much more similar than had hitherto been suspected.

The characters of the hindlimb are well authenticated as the left leg in the British Museum specimen is complete and in its natural position. The femur is 58 mm long, the tibia and fibula 80 mm. This is a reptilian and not a typically avian limb, for there is no tibio-tarsus and the metatarsals are separate. There are, in fact, four tarso-metatarsals. The four toes of the foot are formed by two phalanges in the first, three in the second, and four in the third and fourth, the terminal phalanx in each case being a claw. But the most important feature of the foot is that the first digit (the hallux) is rotated backwards and is consequently capable of being opposed to the others. This means that *Archaeopteryx* could perch and was consequently able to be arboreal.

The skeleton thus shows a remarkable intermingling of reptilian and avian features of great evolutionary interest and this is heightened by the fact that none of the bones was pneumatic.

Whatever doubts of attribution to reptile or to bird there may be concerning the bones, there can be none about the plumage, for even its minute details have been preserved as impressions. The structure of the feathers is shown to be typical of modern flying birds. The London specimen shows quite clearly the primary and secondary quills and coverts of the wing and quills of the tail. The wings were spread out on the principal slab with their dorsal surface originally upwards and the viewer sees the imprint of their undersides.

Sir Gavin de Beer states there are six primaries and ten secondaries, but the clarity of the imprint has not prevented a considerable difference of opinion as to the number of these feathers. In the Eastman-Zittel text-book (1902) it is stated that there were seven primaries and ten secondaries. Gerhard Heilmann (*Origin of Birds*,

1926) published figures of the wings of the Berlin specimen giving twelve primaries, though there is no doubt that several of the impressions were double-struck and these numbers can be reduced. The 1932 edition of Zittel (edited by Sir Arthur Smith Woodward) gives the numbers as seven primaries and ten secondaries. Other researchers over the years have favoured six or seven primaries. However, there seems good reason to suppose that two primaries are missing from the London specimen (D. B. O. Savile, *Auk*, January 1957, pp. 99–101) so that the number of primaries should perhaps be eight. This number is accepted in the recent writings of Roger Tory Peterson.

The tail quills, though typically birdlike, are attached to an equally typically reptilian tail. The feathers extend from the sixth to the twentieth caudal. This makes a feathered tail of about 300 mm long, with a breadth of about 80 mm at the last vertebra. Coverts overlie the bases of those quills which were attached to the sides of the vertebrae. In the Berlin specimen it seems that the tail coverts were continuous with a series of body feathers on the bird's back but nowhere in the London specimen is there any evidence of body or contour feathers.

As a result of his study of *Archaeopteryx lithographica*, Sir Gavin de Beer reached the conclusion that there is no foundation for the theory that *Archaeopteryx* (the British Museum specimen) and the so-called *Archaeornis* (the Berlin Museum specimen) represent the originators respectively of the Ratites and Carinates. Indeed, he went further, and suggested that there is no justification for their differing generic and specific names. Both should be referred to a single species *Archaeopteryx lithographica* (not *A. macrura*).

In 1958 a third skeleton of *Archaeopteryx* was described. It came from the same quarry as the London specimen but from a level some six metres below. This skeleton is less complete than the others and adds nothing to our knowledge of the skull or sternum. It is very close to the London example in its dimensions and characters and confirms that these two are adults while the Berlin specimen is that of a younger individual. The third *Archaeopteryx* is in a museum near the quarry.

H. von Meyer described, in 1857, a new species of *Pterodactylus*, *P. crassipes*, from the Solnhofen Lithographic Limestone near

Riedenburg. The fossil is in Teylers Museum in Haarlem, Holland and was overlooked until September 1970 when John Ostrom of Yale saw the two slabs and recognized not a pterosaur but the earliest specimen of *Archaeopteryx*. Though the skeletal evidence is fragmentary some aspects of it are unusually distinct, as, for example, the long, strongly curved, horny claws on the hand. In general features the specimen appears to agree with the London and Berlin examples.

What conclusions are to be drawn concerning these birds in the story of evolution? First and most obvious is that birds are descended from reptilian ancestors, and the problem becomes the search for an earlier reptile whose skeletal characters would seem to permit a gradual alteration to the features that occur in *Archaeopteryx* and whose mode of life would seem to give promise of such a development. In *Archaeopteryx* we can say that in evolution, as distinct from time, no really great advance had been made in the skeleton from a reptilian stage. The bird was no larger than a raven, so we may look for a reptile ancestor about 30 cm long, with a small skull which has teeth like those of *Archaeopteryx*, whose vertebrae has flattened or very slightly cupped ends, whose front limb was approximately the same length as the hind, and whose thigh-bone length was almost three-quarters the size of the lower hind leg. This last ratio is a matter of some importance in assessing the mode of movement of the animal.

All these features can be found in varying degrees in two great groups of reptiles: the flying reptiles or pterosaurs, which shared very much the same environment as *Archaeopteryx* but whose method of flight was quite dissimilar, and which had hollow bones like modern birds; and the smaller bipedal dinosaurs which could run on their hind legs with the forearms well away from the ground. These have many characters in their skull, limbs and especially in the hip region, that are much like those of the earliest birds. Even so this does not necessarily imply that they were ancestral to the birds, but rather that birds and dinosaurs were both descended from a common ancestor, which researches indicate came from a still earlier group of small bipedal reptiles called Pseudosuchia from the Triassic of Germany, Scotland and South Africa.

Back in the Triassic geological period, about 200 million years ago, there were apparently numerous kinds of small unspecialized

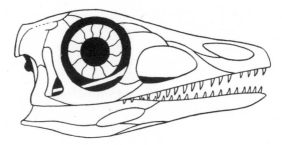

Fig. 11. The hypothetical Proavian. Reconstruction of the skull. About twice
natural size. (After Heilmann.)

reptiles able to run on their hind legs and thus raise the front part
of their body from the ground. We may conclude that in some
geographical conditions there was a certain amount of overcrowding
among populations of this kind and the fight for living-space was
probably considerable. Some may as a consequence have been
attracted to the trees. They already had the ability to balance on
their hind legs, and this would be an asset in running along boughs.
Once there, they would find a hitherto largely untapped source of
insect and plant foods which would encourage them to climb the
branches, wander from branch to branch and ultimately to leap
from stem to stem. This would inevitably result in the development
of the forelimbs into important organs for grasping and balance.
No actual remains of this intermediate form have been discovered
but it has been called the Proavian and restorations of it have been
made (Fig. 11). The new kind of food would probably also lead to
the reduction of the number of teeth (as in fact has happened in
Archaeopteryx). The next step – the gradual development of a branch
jumper into a glider from tree to tree and the gradual growth of
feathers – was probably quite accidental, though there is no fossil
evidence to show how the feather first came into existence.

Dr P. Galton believes that the arboreal 'Proavis' was derived from
a ground-living form, perhaps related to the Ornithischian dinosaurs,
and A. Walker has recently suggested a closer relationship between
the ancestors of crocodiles and birds.

A few theories exist about the gradual fraying of reptilian scales
to make feathers, but no credence can be given to them for a number
of important reasons. The contemporary and very distantly related

pterosaurs flew by means of a thin web of skin – a patagium – attached between the body, the forearm and hand and the hind leg, and these reptiles seem to have lost their scales so that the process may have been related to a heat-regulation mechanism associated with a good blood supply to a thin and unscaly skin. The primitive bird-ancestor may have attained a somewhat similar condition to begin with, though the well-developed flight of the pterosaurs made them much freer of the air than *Archaeopteryx* and, with much of their life spent over the sea or on rocky ledges, they may have needed a mechanism of this kind, whereas *Archaeopteryx*, in the confines of the forest, had a very different and less mechanical kind of flight. In the close arrangement of the vegetation their bough-hopping or gliding habits did not demand the same kind of superficial mechanism, and the keratin covering of the forearms was perhaps some kind of answer. It would almost certainly add to their gliding potentialities. But their long hind-limbs, the long tail and flattened vertebrae all made true flapping flight difficult, though it was this very instability that was to lead to the development of true flight and to the avian backbone and short tufted tail. The essay of an animal into the air demanded a great deal of perception and a high skill in balance to which their arboreal experience had already contributed. The selective effect of these requirements was ultimately responsible for the increase in the size of the eye and orbit and of the brain. The stimulus for flight was the new supply of insect food; in order to catch such food there would need to be a lengthening of the jaws, and with such feeding habits there could be associated that loss of teeth (no longer needed) and the slightly different means of jaw movement leading to snapping ability. These are precisely the changes which took place in the step from reptilian skull to the *Archaeopteryx* head and jaws.

None the less, the stages of evolution we can observe in fossils are based on skeletal evidence alone, and, although it is true that a knowledge of comparative anatomy often suggests physiological probabilities, we have not yet any real knowledge of the way of estimating their relative proportions. It would indeed be extraordinary if, out of the vast range of Mesozoic time, the exact half-way stage of the reptile-bird transition had been discovered.

Apart from *Archaeopteryx*, remains of Jurassic birds are very doubtful. Professor O. C. Marsh in 1881 described a crushed skull from the Morrison (Upper Jurassic) Formation of Wyoming which he named *Laopteryx priscus*. The hinder region of the skull shows well-marked and sometimes open sutures. The identification of the specimen has never been satisfactory although it has been referred to a bird of uncertain systematic position. More probably it is part of a reptilian skull.

In 1955 Dr Luis Ferrer published a preliminary note (with figure) on the presence of a small bird feather in Upper Jurassic rocks of the Sierra del Montsech, Spain. The figure shows certain similarities to the feather of *Archaeopteryx*.

Alleged footprints of *Archaeopteryx* have been described from Solnhofen and others from the same formation have been given the names of *Protornis bavarica, Hypornithes* and *Ornithichnites,* but all of these are only doubtfully attributable to birds and are more satisfactorily regarded as synonyms of *Kouphichnium*, a dinosaurian tridactyl footprint.

The systematic position of *Archaeopteryx* can be given as:
Subclass Archaeornithes; Ancestral Birds.
Order Archaeopterygiformes.
Family Archaeopterygidae, *Archaeopteryx* (fossil).

5. Cretaceous birds

There is a great gap in time between the Jurassic *Archaeopteryx* and the next birds in the fossil record. The circumstances in which the respective remains are met with do, however, help to explain this. *Archaeopteryx* was preserved in the fine mud of a great inland sea. The Cretaceous remains, with very few exceptions, were fossilized in the fine sea oozes that later consolidated into chalk. All these birds were therefore accidental captures of some ooze, silt or mud in water.

On land, in the interval of nearly fifty-five million years, an immense amount of bird evolution must have taken place, but, as we know from our experience today, the fragile remains of birds would be scattered on the ground or in the undergrowth and quickly destroyed by scavengers, or by surface erosion.

A Lower Cretaceous freshwater lake in South Gippsland, Victoria, Australia, produced three feathers in 1966. The latest to be described (by M. Waldman of Ottawa) is 15 mm long and 6 mm at its broadest. It may be a covert, but of an unknown bird.

In the upper half of the Cretaceous we find the remains of 23 species of interesting birds, a very few of them alleged still to be toothed. Two of them, *Ichthyornis* and *Hesperornis* from the Upper Cretaceous of Kansas, are figured in almost every text-book of palaeontology. There are others, mostly from the same locality and of the same age, but including also a representative from England and another from South America. *Ichthyornis* and *Hesperornis* were first described and figured by Professor O. C. Marsh, of Yale University (*Odontornithes, a monograph of the extinct toothed birds of North America*, 1880) and they attained a world-wide fame, though it is sometimes overlooked that more recent studies, especially by Dr J. T. Gregory, also of Yale, have modified some of Marsh's views.

Ichthyornis ('the fish-bird' – see Frontispiece) was just over 20 cm (eight inches) in height and is said to have lived after the manner of a tern. Its skeleton (Fig. 12) shows well the typically modern appearance, especially the large and prominent keel on the sternum. There can be no doubt that this was a true bird capable of strong flight as

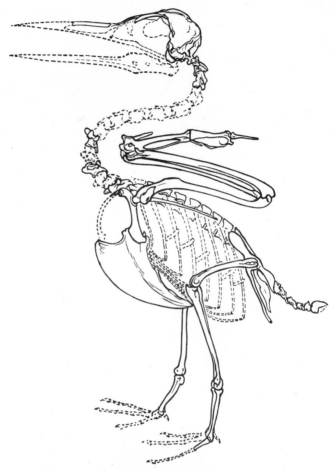

Fig. 12. *Ichthyornis victor*. Reconstruction of skeleton. About half natural size. (After Marsh.)

understood today. Some years ago there were interesting developments concerning its jaws with alleged teeth, because Dr J. T. Gregory in a re-examination of the type material found that the lower jaw furnished with teeth agrees in the smallest details with those of the swimming reptiles known as mosasaurs, and the upper jaw fragments, showing alveoli, are so indeterminate that neither

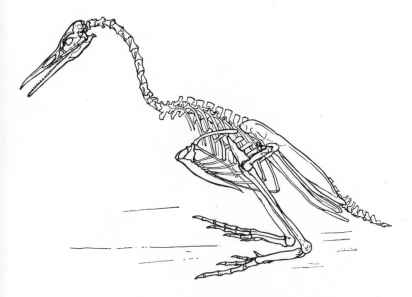

Fig. 13. *Hesperornis regalis*. About one-fifteenth natural size. Skeleton drawn by Maurice Wilson.

their nature nor their origin can be established. The Niobrara Chalk is very rich in mosasaur remains so that the chance association of their jaws with a bird skeleton is possible. It can now only be said that *Ichthyornis* was a Cretaceous flying bird with well-developed wings and undoubted powers of flight, but whether it was toothed we do not know.

On the other hand, its contemporary *Hesperornis* (Plate 4 and Fig. 14) has continued with undiminished prestige. This large bird was over 180 cm from tip of the beak to the end of the tail, and its skull and skeleton (Fig. 13) are fairly well known from several specimens now in the Peabody Museum of Yale University, in the Museum of Natural History, Kansas University, and in the American Museum of Natural History.

The skeleton is well developed, but has one obvious peculiarity: the weakness of the shoulder girdle. Fig. 13 shows that there is no keel on the breast-bone, indicating that the powers of flight must have been poor; but the arm shows that they were, in fact,

Fig. 14. *Hesperornis regalis*. About one-fifteenth natural size. Reconstruction by Maurice Wilson.

non-existent. The thin pendant process shown in the figure between the sternum and the patella is the humerus and, although the bone is almost 15 cm (6 in) long, it is so thin that it is almost certain that no distal bones, radius or ulna, articulated with it. The wing could only have been degenerate with absolutely no flying ability, although humeral feathers might have been developed. There is a point at dispute here. Many artists picture, and most books refer to, *Hesperornis* as being wingless and feature it as a remarkable bird, with not a vestige of a wing, but with only two limbs, the highly developed swimming legs. This is certainly not justified, for there is no reason to assume that the humerus, encased in contour feathers at least, did not form a small external feature. It had, of course, nothing like the bony structure of the arm of a penguin (cf. Fig. 21).

The hind limbs were so highly adapted for swimming that it is doubtful if they could have been used for walking on land. *Hesperornis* gives additional proof, therefore, that birds had attained a high degree of specialization by the Upper Cretaceous.

PLATE 4. *Hesperornis regalis.* From a drawing by Maurice Wilson.

It is important that the skull should be briefly described, for, as illustrations show, its general structure is typically avian, but there is an upper jaw, with fourteen teeth in its hinder half (the maxilla), and associated with a long rather rod-like lower jaw (Fig. 15) along which thirty-three teeth are said to be placed in a groove, like those of ichthyosaurs. Naturally these jaws have been submitted to a detailed study in view of the recent findings on the alleged *Ichthyornis* jaws. As a result there has been found a remarkable similarity between the bird lower jaw and that of mosasaurs. But whereas the '*Ichthyornis*' jaws show no differentiation from those of the mosasaur *Clidastes*, the lower jaw of *Hesperornis* is stated to have undoubted avian features akin to those of divers, in spite of the absence of a symphysis and the presence of teeth of reptilian form in the dentary. However, the writer has examined the type and other specimens in Yale and is of the opinion that there is no satisfactory association of the lower jaw with the skull fragments. The lower jaw might very well be that of a mosasaur, and certainly has the joint in the mandible characteristic of these reptiles. Furthermore the allegedly toothed part of the maxilla of the type-specimen is indeterminate in position and source. It might very well also be mosasaurian and is by no means assuredly avian.

Some years ago, however, the writer saw, in the Nebraska State Museum, a lower jaw with teeth unquestionably associated with *Hesperornis* remains. This specimen was sent to London and was drawn by Mr Maurice Wilson for Fig. 16. There is also a toothed specimen of a smaller species in the Natural History Museum of Kansas University with a well-attested history. The teeth are not like those figured in Marsh's 1880 drawings, which as we have seen are closely similar to those of the mosasaur *Clidastes*. It might be objected that the similarities figured by Marsh were due to convergence, to the same kind of life and feeding habits in the same sort of environment. But this is not a positive argument and in any case receives no support from the fish-eating reptiles of similar habits.

Other birds whose remains are known from the richly fossiliferous Niobrara Chalk of Kansas include *Baptornis advenus*, which was first described in 1877 by Professor Marsh on a tarso-metatarsus. Subsequently other bones have been found and figured, but none has been found of the skull. The original bird must have been the size

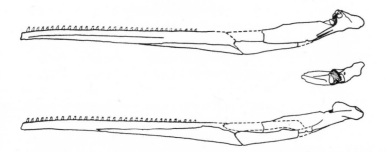

Fig. 15. Reconstruction of a lower jaw referred to *Hesperornis regalis*, but believed by the writer to be possibly that of a mosasaur. Lateral view (above); medial view (below). Upper view of articular cotylus (middle). About half natural size. (After J. T. Gregory.)

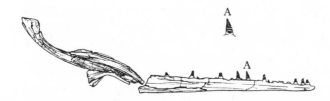

Fig. 16. *Hesperornis regalis*. Incomplete lower jaw from the University of Nebraska Collection. About one-third natural size. A, tooth enlarged. Drawn by Maurice Wilson.

of a diver like *Gavia* and have had quite strong affinities with *Hesperornis*. Both an ulna and a radius have been found which are at Yale. Closely related are the species of *Lonchodytes* from the Lance Formation of Wyoming.

Apatornis celer, first thought to be *Ichthyornis*, was described under its present name in 1873; the original specimens are also at Yale University. Like the others it came from the Yellow Chalk at Smoky Hill River, in Western Kansas. Quite a number of vertebrae, parts of the shoulder girdle and pelvis, and limb bones have been found, exhibiting different degrees of similarity to *Ichthyornis*. The bird does not appear to have been as well developed a flyer as its more famous contemporary. From the same source comes *Hargeria gracilis*, of which there is one skeleton in the National Museum, Washington, several skeletons in Yale University, and various bones in the Natural History Museum of Kansas University. It is very closely related to *Hesperornis* and was, in fact, described under that name in 1876. It does not seem to have been toothed.

Professor Marsh also founded the genus *Cimolopteryx* with two species, *Cimolopteryx rara* and *Cimolopteryx* (now *Apatornis*) *retusa*, both from the Cretaceous Laramie Formation of Converse County, Wyoming. They are known only from shoulder bones in the Peabody Museum, Yale, which are of uncertain relationship. They seem to represent birds the size of a pigeon. Other species have been described from the Lance Formation of Wyoming as well as a related genus, *Ceramornis*.

In 1858 Lucas Barrett, of the then Woodwardian Museum in Cambridge, discovered bones of a bird in the Cambridge Greensand at Coldham Common between Grantchester and Cambridge. Of these a dorsal vertebra and some hindlimb bones were referred to a new genus and species, *Pelagornis sedgwicki*, in 1864, but the genus was later renamed *Enaliornis*, as the name *Pelagornis* had already been used for a different animal. Subsequently a large part of the skeleton including the hinder parts of the skull, but not the jaws, was discovered and eventually the remains were named *Enaliornis barretti* by Professor H. G. Seeley in 1869. These birds appear to have been little larger than a pigeon and were almost certainly swimming birds. Little is known of them, however, and no additional finds seem to have been made although their geological age warrants them a high place in the history of birds. In Sweden two Cretaceous birds are known, *Scaniornis lundgreni*, of which humerus, coracoid and scapula have been found, and *Parascaniornis stensiöi* of which there is only a vertebra. These two birds may be ancestral flamingoes. *Torotix clemensi*, also a possible flamingo, has been described from the Lance (Upper Cretaceous) of Wyoming.

From France comes a femur of Neocomian age that has been called *Gallornis* and which is perhaps related to the Swedish genera. Bones from the hind leg of an ancestral cormorant from the Danian of Transylvania have been named *Elopteryx*. Another Cretaceous swimming bird is represented by a tarso-metatarsus from South Chile. This bone is now in Kiel University Museum and has been named *Neogaeornis wetzeli* by Karl Lambrecht.

The fourteen Cretaceous birds so far mentioned no doubt owe

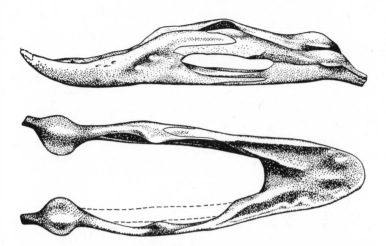

Fig. 17. *Caenagnathus collinsi*. The lower jaw, outer view (above) and dorsal view (below). About half natural size. (After R. M. Sternberg.)

their preservation to their swimming habits which allowed their bones after death to be covered in silt, but there is a single possible survivor of the land forms of the time. This bird is represented by an almost complete lower jaw from the Upper Cretaceous of Alberta, Canada. It was fully described by R. M. Sternberg in 1940 as *Caenagnathus collinsi*. The type jaw is reproduced here as Fig. 17. The length of the jaw is almost 23 cm, so that the total size of the whole bird must have been considerable. The jaw shows an interesting and even important series of features. The anterior end with its fused dentaries and the hinder end with double articular faects are typical of later birds, as is the absence of teeth, yet the open sutures between the other bones and the presence of a large mandibular foramen and the general shape show dinosaurian affinities. The large size of the mandible is held to indicate that the bird was proportionately large and was probably a runner. It may have occupied an upland habitat where it would be both companion and competitor to many well-known dinosaurs. It may, however, be an ornithomimid dinosaur and Wetmore has withdrawn it from his classification (see below).

In 1964 the head of an avian right ulna was found in the Upper

Cretaceous of Alberta. It is now in the Royal Ontario Museum, Toronto. It appears to come from a large limb.

Looking at the Cretaceous birds as a whole one sees the series as very different from that usually portrayed. Only one of them (i.e. *Hesperornis*) now seems to have possessed teeth and the characters of true birds are more conspicuous than the relics of their reptilian ancestry. Differentiation was already well advanced. *Hesperornis* had become an entirely water-living bird, *Caenagnathus* seems to have been a wholly terrestrial runner, and in the next geological era, the Tertiary, many modern lines of specialization were early apparent.

6. Tertiary birds

In the Eocene, the first period of the Tertiary, many of the kinds of birds now living were already represented and the group became rapidly diversified. Of the thirty-one orders of birds now alive fourteen are represented. Thus it is no longer possible to proceed bird by bird in this series and they must be described under their present classification so that their family record may be seen more clearly. The classification adopted is that of Dr Alexander Wetmore published in 1960.*

By Eocene times the major division of birds into those which fly, i.e. Carinates, and those which are flightless and run, i.e. Ratites, had been made, although the evidence for the former is much greater than for the latter and it may be argued that the latter do not form a natural order. The reason for this difference in representation again lies in their respective habitats, for although there are numerous Eocene representatives of the flying birds, they are mostly those, like the pelicans, herons, cranes and gulls, which lived in watery surroundings that often led to the burying of their remains in mud and thus favoured permanent preservation.

Among the flightless running birds, the emus, *Aepyornis* and the moas, few have relatives in the Eocene. In the Museum there is a small piece of a limb bone, named *Eremopezus eocaenus*, from the Eocene of the Fayum; it may well be from an ancestor of *Aepyornis*. The *Aepyornis* material is of much later date and comes from the Pleistocene and Holocene of Madagascar. The remains are well known but their ancestry is obscure, though the Eocene fragment referred to above, part of a tarso-metatarsus from the Oligocene of the Fayum (*Stromeria fajumensis*), and pieces of possibly aepyornid egg-shell named *Psammornis rothschildi* from the Eocene of southern Algeria, all suggest that the concentration of species in Madagascar was the last stand of birds once distributed much more widely.

Aepyornis with the smaller *Mullerornis*, the so-called elephant-birds, belong to a special Order, the Aepyornithiformes. Most of the

---

* A Classification for the Birds of the World. *Smithson. misc. Collns*, **139**, 11.

members of the genus *Aepyornis* were large and massive but they had small skulls (Plate 5). Their feet normally have four toes, though the hallux is sometimes missing. The largest species is *Aepyornis titan*, a little over 3 metres (10 ft) high. The size of this great bird probably inspired some of the legends of the past such as that of the Rukh, or Roc, of Sinbad the Sailor and Marco Polo, for Arab traders have been familiar for centuries with the coast of Madagascar.

The eggs of *Aepyornis* are still found buried in the sand on the shores where they were laid in Pleistocene times. The real egg is certainly nothing like the dome-house that Sinbad took fifty paces to walk around. None the less, eggs of *Aepyornis* are always of interest, for they are not infrequently washed out of the beaches or out of the sandy soil near lakes in Madagascar and have reached many museums where their great size attracts attention. The largest specimen in the Palaeontological Department of this Museum measures 90 cm (3 ft) in its largest circumference and 75 cm in girth, so that its liquid content would be over nine litres. Some of the eggs contain the bones of embryos. Much has been made of the relative size of these eggs and of the birds that presumably laid them, but study of eggs of other birds such as *Apteryx*, as well as of the dinosaurs, shows that there is great variation in the size and nature of the shells.

The first fossil flightless birds to be discovered were those called moas, a name derived from Maori legends, for these large creatures seem to have lingered on until the arrival of Maoris in the fourteenth and even white men in the eighteenth century. Their nature was first deduced by Richard Owen, Director of the Museum, on the evidence of a single thigh bone. He subsequently gave the name *Dinornis struthioides* ('huge bird like an ostrich') to this kind of bird. A great many other bones belonging to this species have since been found in New Zealand but nearly all of them are of Pleistocene age or Recent, only a few dating back to the Pliocene. Many other kinds were found in caves, in swamps and in native refuse heaps and occasionally complete skeletons, feathers, and traces of skin have been found, so that the structure of the birds is quite well known.

Moas (Order Dinornithiformes) were quite unable to fly for they had no front limb, not even a socket on the shoulder girdle for it. The shoulder girdle itself was reduced. In contrast the hind limbs

PLATE 5. *Aepyornis maximus*, an Elephant-bird. Height over 210 cm. From a drawing by Maurice Wilson.

PLATE 6. *Dinornis maximus*, a New Zealand Moa. Restoration by Maurice Wilson.

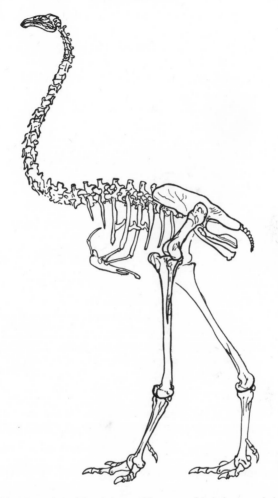

Fig. 18. *Dinornis maximus*. The skeleton. About one-thirtieth natural size. Drawn by Maurice Wilson.

were massively developed and the birds seem to have been good runners. The feathers appear in structure to be closer to those of Australian flightless birds than to those of the New Zealand kiwis, though the moas were confined to New Zealand. The largest moa was *Dinornis maximus* which was nearly 3·5 metres (12 ft) high (Plate 6 and Fig. 18). Other forms of moas were *Euryapteryx elephantopus* with very stout legs: *Euryapteryx gravipes* was smaller and *Anomalopteryx didiformis*, *A. parva*, and *Megalapteryx didina* were smaller still, *A. parva* being only 90 cm (3 ft) high. *Megalapteryx*, of which a complete skeleton was found in a cave on South Island, was rather like *Anomalopteryx*. All these kinds were no doubt well adapted to their habitat and many of them seem to have lived on ferns, but the evidence of Maori refuse heaps suggests that they were hunted out of existence. Today the sole surviving flightless bird of this kind in New Zealand is the kiwi, *Apteryx* (Order Apterygiformes), a bird about the size of a chicken with a long beak, very small wings concealed by the curious body feathers, no tail, and four-toed feet. It is unique among living birds in having its nostrils at the end of the beak and not immediately in front of the eyes. So far its remains have only been found in sub-Recent deposits.

The Order Casuariiformes is represented by the unique emu (*Dromaeus*) of Australia, of which many species have been described, and the cassowaries (*Casuarius*) from New Guinea and Northern Australia. The oldest of the remains attributable to this order are from the Pliocene and Pleistocene of Australia (*Dromornis* and *Genyornis*). *Hypselornis*, a genus known only by a phalangeal bone, rather doubtfully avian, comes from the Pliocene of India. These kinds of birds seem to have been distributed more widely in the past than they are now.

All the rheas (Order Rheiformes) are restricted to southern South America and most of the fossil remains come from Argentina. *Protorhea* and *Heterorhea* are genera from the Lower Pleistocene. *Rhea* itself, the living form, is also found as a fossil in the Pampean (Pleistocene) formation.

Ostriches (Order Struthioniformes), now confined to Africa and Arabia, were once widely distributed over south-eastern Europe, India and China, surviving in the last named country until historical times. A Pliocene ostrich occurs in India, and *Eleutherornis*, from the Eocene of Switzerland, is also probably an ostrich. The Ratites are further considered in Chapter VII.

These Ratites were by no means the only birds that had ceased to practise flight. *Diatryma* (Order Diatrymiformes, Fig. 19 and Plate 7), for example, a gigantic running ground bird from the Eocene of

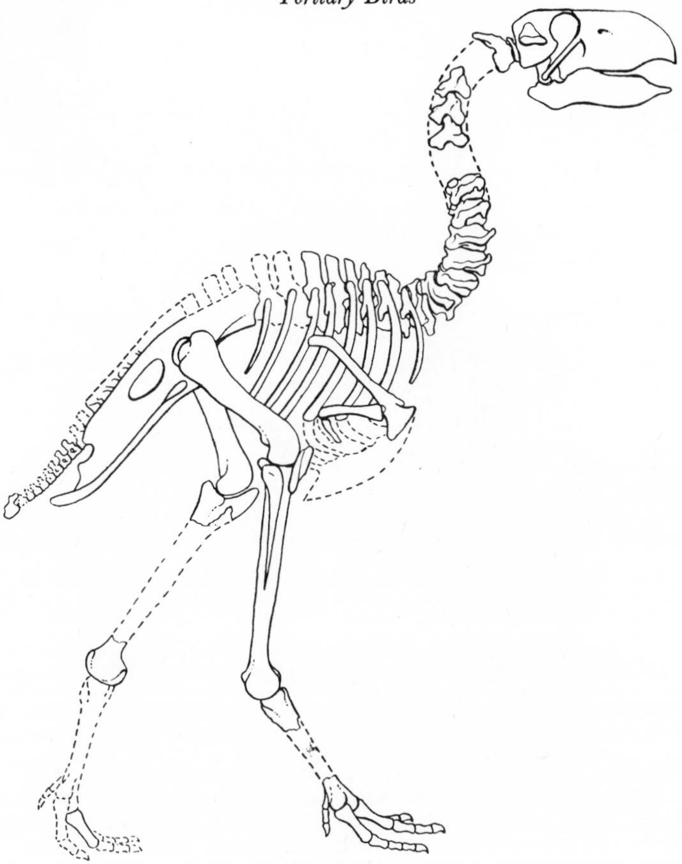

Fig. 19. Skeleton of *Diatryma steini*. Lower Eocene of Wyoming, U.S.A. About one-eighteenth natural size. (After Mathew & Granger.)

Wyoming and New Mexico, has been described as 'one of the land marks of avian palaeontology'. A plaster cast of the skeleton of *Diatryma steini*, from the Lower Eocene of Wyoming, which was over 2 metres (about 7 ft) high, is in the Museum. With strong and heavy legs and a large head with a very powerful beak, these birds must have proved serious rivals to the mammals of their day. *Diatryma* is known only from the United States but there were somewhat similar flightless birds in the Eocene of Great Britain and the Continent.

PLATE 7. *Diatryma steini*. From a drawing by Maurice Wilson.

Gastornis, though as large as an ostrich, has affinities with geese rather than with ostriches and probably belongs to this group. Its remains are known from the Eocene of Belgium, France and England. *Remiornis* from the Eocene of France, and *Dasornis* from the London Clay of Sheppey, are other genera included in the group on less satisfactory material.

The Eocene saw very many birds that had fully developed powers of flight. Indeed, about half of the remaining orders of birds have Eocene representatives. To describe these in detail would be beyond the scope of a work such as this, but some forms may be mentioned as illustrative of the main orders in Wetmore's classification.

The divers (Order Gaviiformes) have *Colymboides anglicus*, which is known from a sternum in the British Museum (Natural History). This was found in the Upper Eocene or Oligocene of Hampshire and the bird seems to have been intermediate between the loons and the grebes. The grebes (Podicepiformes) have, however, no member earlier than *Colymbus* from the Oligocene of Oregon. Albatrosses (Procellariiformes) have *Puffinus* in the Oligocene of Europe and in the Miocene of South Carolina but the pelicans (Pelecaniformes) are generously represented quite early in the Tertiary. *Argillornis longipennis* and *Prophaethon shrubsolei* are found in the London Clay. The latter was a tropic bird considerably larger than the living *Phaethon*. From the Upper Eocene of Hordwell, Hampshire comes *Actiornis*. A cormorant (*Phalacrocorax*) and a snake-bird (*Ahinga*) have recently been reported from the Miocene of Tunisia.

Exceptionally well preserved remains of a gigantic 'toothed' marine bird, *Osteodontornis orri* from the Miocene of California, are classed by H. Howard with the somewhat similar forms *Pseudo-dontornis longirostris* from the Miocene of South Carolina and *P. stirtoni* from the ? Miocene of New Zealand in a family of the Pelecaniformes. To this group the skull and bones in the Museum named *Odontopteryx toliapicus* from the London Clay are also referable (Fig. 20). In these forms the 'teeth' are not true teeth but are bony outgrowths (serrations) of the jawbones.

Dr Wetmore places the penguins in a separate superorder of birds (Impennes) comparable to the so-called Toothed Birds (Odontognathae) of the Cretaceous and the whole of the Neognathae as outlined in the rest of this chapter, but Professor A. S. Romer

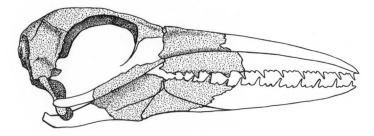

Fig. 20. *Odontopteryx toliapicus.* Skull and lower jaw from the Eocene of Sheppey. Two-thirds natural size.

includes them as the Order Sphenisciformes between the albatrosses and petrels and the pelican group. The geological history of these attractive birds is of great interest and there are diverse opinions as to their origin. Some authorities regard the penguins as highly modified for their aquatic life, whereas others regard them as being merely diverted from life in one medium (the air) to another, the sea. Some writers claim that penguins are clearly the descendants of flightless terrestrial birds that have taken to the water; others see them, and equally clearly, as derived from marine flying birds. In any case their wings are quite useless for flight, but are valuable aids for swimming. In the legs the metatarsal bones are not completely fused, as they are in all other groups of typical birds described here. The foot is webbed.

The penguins had already acquired their present habit by Eocene times and apart from individual size and geographical distribution they were very similar to those that are so familiar to us today. The earliest known forms of penguins are from the Eocene and Oligocene of New Zealand, and many genera of their successors, all from marine sediments, have been described, in particular from the Lower Miocene of Patagonia. *Spheniscus* has been described from the Pliocene of South Africa.

Most penguins are confined to Antarctic lands and waters. None has crossed the Equator naturally. In the Northern Hemisphere the auks, especially the Great Auk, are probably more closely related to the penguins than has been generally realized. There is also a very considerable similarity between the general skeletal structure of the penguins and the Procellariiformes (albatrosses and petrels).

Fig. 21. The decline in the size of the penguins. The man on the left is 1·8 m (6 ft) tall. Outlined are Miocene penguins of the genera *Pachydyptes* and *Anthropornis* represented in the first figure, and another Miocene form *Palaeeudyptes* for the second. Then follows the largest of the living forms, the Emperor Penguin, *Aptenodytes forsteri*, and, in outline, one of the moderate sized Miocene penguins, *Palaeospheniscus patagonicus*. Last in the line is the Galapagos Penguin, *Spheniscus mendiculus*. The drawing shows only the relative size and not the characters of the penguins. (Modified from G. G. Simpson.)

Early in the Tertiary, the ancestors of the penguins were not only able to fly in the air but could also use their wings in the water. Eventually they lost the power of flight and became swimming creatures that use their wings for swimming instead of flying. The penguin wing is thus not a secondary structure but a true wing re-adapted for a new medium. The major differences between penguins and other birds follow upon this mode of life: the feet are used in swimming and the ability of these birds to stand erect is derived from this facility rather than from any terrestrial ancestry. The completeness in the feather covering and the protective layer of blubber beneath the skin are modifications for swimming in cold water that have their parallels in other animal groups.

Much of the interest in fossil penguins is due to the exaggerated size frequently attributed to them, based on calculations of the relative lengths of the fossil bones compared with those of the living Emperor Penguin (*Aptenodytes forsteri*), which is just over 90 cm (3 ft) in height. The sizes of fossil and Recent penguins are compared in Fig. 21, from which it will be seen that the largest known fossil forms (*Pachydyptes* and *Anthropornis*) were 160 cm (5 ft 4 in) and 150 cm (5 ft) respectively in height. Dr G. G. Simpson (*Fossil Penguins*,

American Museum of Natural History, 1946; and *Rec. S. Aust. Mus.*
13 (1), 1957) deals with all aspects of these problems.

The Order Ciconiiformes, which includes the herons, storks and
bitterns, has some Eocene representatives in *Proherodius*, a heron,
from the London Clay, and *Agnopterus*, a flamingo, from the Upper
Eocene of the Paris Basin. *Telmabates antiquus*, a wading bird from
the Eocene of Patagonia, described by Dr Hildegarde Howard,
appears to be related to the flamingoes and thus to be referable to
this order. There are other related Cretaceous and Eocene genera
from Wyoming. An early ibis is *Ibidopsis* from the Upper Eocene of
Hordwell, Hampshire.

Ducks and geese (Order Anseriformes) have a long ancestry, for
there are *Romainvillea*, possible ancestor of the geese, from the Upper
Eocene of the Paris Basin, and *Eonessa* in the Middle Eocene of Utah.
True geese (*Anser*) appeared in Europe in the Miocene, in Asia in
the Pliocene and arrived in North America in the Pleistocene. Not
all the fossils of this kind were fliers because *Cnemiornis calcitrans* from
the Pleistocene of New Zealand was large and flightless. Incidentally
this bird illustrates the difficulty and the danger of attempting to
name bird bones on too slender evidence or on isolated remains.
The tibia of *Cnemiornis* was considered by Richard Owen to be that
of a moa; its sternum was believed by Parker to be from a rail but
the discovery of the skull showed that the bird was a goose.

Vultures (Order Falconiformes) have long been scavenging or
preying on their contempories. *Lithornis vulturinus*, the oldest known,
was first collected from the London Clay of Sheppey by the famous
anatomist John Hunter. *Neocathartes grallator*, another rapacious
terrestrial bird, comes from the Upper Eocene of Wyoming. Most
of the fossils of this order date from the Oligocene. The alleged
presence of *Aquila* and *Falco* in the Eocene is very doubtful indeed.
One of the best known vultures is the Pleistocene *Teratornis*, from
the Rancho La Brea tar pits of Los Angeles, California.

The members of the Order Galliformes, comprising the pheasants
and fowls and the unique hoatzins, are mainly more recent geo-
logically, but there are two forms, *Gallinuloides* and *Palaeophasianus*,
recorded from the Middle Eocene of Wyoming. *Paraortyx* and *Palae-
ortyx* from the Upper Eocene of France appear to be partridge-like
birds. The hoatzin (*Opisthocomus cristatus*) is known only from tropical

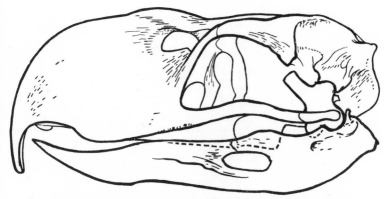

Fig. 22. *Phororhacos longissimus*. Restored skull and lower jaw from the Miocene of Patagonia. About one-quarter natural size. Drawn by Maurice Wilson.

South America and is the sole member of its family. In the nestling the thumb is large and bears a claw which, with the only other clawed finger, enables it to climb, but the adult bird loses the claw from the thumb. The hoatzin is well known because of this peculiarity. Its geological history is confined to recent times.

The Order Gruiformes comprising the cranes, rails, and a number of most interesting flightless birds, has a long geological history. Fossil rails are common, among the first of them being *Gypsornis* from the Upper Eocene of the Paris Basin. Other forms are *Graculavus* and *Telmatornis* from the Eocene of New Jersey. *Aletornis* comes from the Eocene of Wyoming. *Palaeorallus* and *Eocrex* are from the Eocene of Wyoming and Colorado and are true rails. Milne-Edwards' *Rallus intermedius* from the Ludian stage of the Upper Eocene of Montmartre has been renamed *Quercyrallus ludianus* by Brodkorb (1963). Most of these birds were waders and heavily built fliers but included in this order are the bustards of Europe and the cariamas of South America. The latter have fossil representatives of Oligocene age that seem to have been similarly restricted in flying ability. Associated with them, and probably fairly closely related to them, especially from Miocene times, were several large and powerful flightless birds. *Phororhacos* (Fig. 22, Plate 8) is a well-known example. Its skeleton is 150 cm (5 ft) high, the skull is large

PLATE 8. *Phororhacos inflatus*, the smaller of two known species from Patagonia, about 150 cm high. Restoration by Maurice Wilson.

(about 45 cm (18 in) long) with a very powerful beak, and the legs are characteristically long. This is another instance of the successful adaptation of a bird to terrestrial life in the absence of competition from mammalian carnivores. More recent and even more robust birds of this kind are *Brontornis* and *Liornis*, also South American, of which the Museum has foot bones.

Notornis, a modern flightless bird and a true rail, was first known from its bones. These were found with moa remains at Wain-gongoro, North Island, in 1848. In the following year, Walter Mantell, son of the great Sussex palaeontologist, saw the skin of a newly-killed bird hanging up in a Maori village near Dusky Bay at the southern end of New Zealand and realized that it belonged to the same kind of bird. He sent it to London, where it is now exhibited in the Bird Gallery of the Museum. Maori sealers had caught the bird and had roasted and eaten it, as no doubt they had killed and eaten many more. *Notornis* is unable to fly because of its small wings. At one time it was common in New Zealand but its numbers fell until it was thought to be extinct. In 1948 a colony of less than 100 birds was discovered in a remote mountain valley near Lake Te Anau in South Island. It is probable that the diatrymas (see p. 46) are closely related to this group.

The gulls, auks, terns and sandpipers, all marine or shore birds, are placed together in the Order Charadriiformes. The long-winged forms, that is the gulls and terns, whose method of life predisposed their remains to preservation in marine conditions, are known from the Eocene onwards, as are the non-flying and short-winged auks. The Great Auk (Plate 9), which looks like a penguin and is the penguin of 'Penguin Island' by Anatole France, used to swim in the North Atlantic but became extinct in comparatively recent times. In the Pliocene there were several auks with a wing nearer to the condition of the penguin that that of the Great Auk.

Pigeons and doves are mostly vegetarian forest birds and live in surroundings in which the rapid decay or destruction of the body precludes most chances of preservation. They are not represented in the early Tertiary and, although there are Miocene forms, pigeons do not become at all common until the Pleistocene. One very specialized, flightless pigeon is, however, well known. This is the Dodo (*Raphus cucullatus*, better known by its former name, *Didus ineptus*).

PLATE 9. *Pinguinus impennis*, the Great Auk, about 50 cm high. Extinct about 1844, its remains are known from the Pleistocene of Gibraltar and Italy. Reconstruction.

Its portraits by the Dutch artist Rolandt Savery are well known (Plate 10). Skeletons (see Fig. 23) and reconstructions of its living appearance are in several museums, and can be seen in the Bird Gallery of this Museum. Original specimens are, however, very rare and the story has often been told of the destruction at Oxford of one of the last specimens. This had been in the collections of Elias Ashmole, and as it had become dishevelled and moth-eaten in 1755 its destruction was ordered by the Vice-Chancellor and Proctors of Oxford University. Happily, the museum curator cut off its head and a foot as mementoes and these remains, together with a foot in the Natural History Museum in London and a head in Copenhagen, are all that are left of specimens once seen as live animals. Between 1610 and 1640, living specimens were exhibited in this country and in Europe, and in 1630 Peter Mundy, the celebrated traveller, saw two dodos in Surat, India. A picture of a living dodo, painted in 1650 by Ustad Mansur, is now in Leningrad. At that time the bird was abundant in Mauritius, flourishing in the absence of ground competition, but it was hunted by sailors for food, even though contemporary accounts say that the flesh was not very palatable, and pigs are said to have destroyed its eggs. It was also entirely without means of defence and only laid one egg at nesting time. These factors ensured its extinction – apart from the bird's trusting-ness which was mistaken for stupidity. The Reunion Dodo, *Raphus apterornis*, is known only from drawings and not by a single bone. The Solitaire, *Pezophaps solitarius*, allied to the dodo, is known only from the small island of Rodriguez. Our information about it in the living state is derived wholly from the evidence of François Leguat, who with a party of French refugees landed in 1691 upon this un-inhabited island and remained there for more than two years. The bird has now been long extinct but numerous bones have been found in the caves of the island which help to corroborate every detail of Leguat's account, even to the 'little round mass' of bone on the wing 'as big as a musket ball' with which the males fought.

The related Orders of the parrots and cuckoos (Psittaciformes and Cuculiformes respectively) date from the Oligocene. Both are anatomically interesting in having a zygodactylous foot, in which the first and fourth toes are turned backwards, giving a claw-hammer kind of structure to the four-toed foot. The oldest parrots

PLATE 10. *Raphus cucullatus*, the Dodo, about 60 cm high. Extinct about 1695, this wingless relative of the pigeon was painted by Rolandt Savery in 1750.

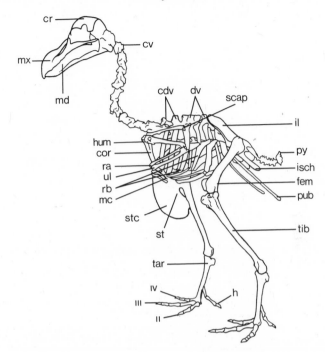

Fig. 23. Skeleton of the Dodo. About one-sixth natural size. *cdv*, cervico-dorsal vertebrae; *cor*, coracoid; *cr*, cranium; *cv*, cervical vertebrae; *dv*, dorsal vertebrae; *fem*, femur; *h*, hallux; *hum*, humerus; *il*, ilium; *isch*, ischium; *md*, mandible; *mc*, metacarpals; *mx*, maxilla; *pub*, pubis; *py*, pygostyle; *ra*, radius; *rb*, ribs; *scap*, scapula; *st*, sternum; *stc*, crest of sternum; *tar*, tarso-metatarsus; *tib*, tibiotarsus; *ul*, ulna; II, III, IV, second, third and fourth digits. Drawn by Maurice Wilson.

are *Archaeopsittacus* in the Upper Oligocene of France and *Conuropsis* in the Miocene of Nebraska. Fossil cuckoos are rare, *Dynamopterus* from the Oligocene of France being the oldest known form.

On the other hand, the owls (Order Strigiformes), which are nocturnal carnivores with forwardly directed eyes and thus distinct from the falcon group of birds, have a long history and several fossil genera. *Protostrix* (= *Minerva*) from the Eocene of Wyoming is the earliest owl. *Asio* and *Bubo* come from the slightly younger Phosphorites of Quercy, France.

Many of the remaining orders of birds are very poorly represented in the fossil record but this would be expected from their habitats.

The goatsuckers (Order Caprimulgiformes) date from the Oligocene of Europe with *Caprimulgus* itself.

Aegialornis, from the Oligocene of France, is the oldest known swift, but no humming-birds are known as fossils. Both kinds of birds are classed under the Order Apodiformes.

The colies (Order Coliiformes), small African birds, are unknown as fossils, and the Order Coraciiformes, which comprises hornbills, kingfishers, rollers and bee-eaters, is but doubtfully of geological antiquity. The rollers are first represented, in the Oligocene of France, by *Geranopterus alatus*. *Halcyornis toliapicus*, of which the Museum has a fragmentary skull and humerus, was found in the London Clay of Sheppey and may be related to the rollers.

The trogons (Order Trogoniformes) are forest birds of the tropics with a peculiar foot in which the first and second toes are turned back. The oldest trogons are *Archaeotrogon* and *Paratrogon* from the Oligocene of France.

The Order Piciformes includes the zygodactylous woodpeckers and the toucans, all birds noted for their strength of bill structure. Only the former have a long geological history, for *Uintornis* from the Eocene of Wyoming appears to be an early woodpecker. Other genera (*Cryptornis*, *Palaeopicus*, *Picus* and *Homalopus*) appear in the Oligocene, Miocene and Pliocene.

Half of all living birds belong to the perching birds (Order Passeriformes). Their success may be largely due to their development of a highly efficient perching foot in which the first toe is in opposition to the other three. Nearly all the passeres are arboreal and highly adapted for flight. The earliest shrikes (*Lanius*) and wagtails (*Motacilla*) were found in the Upper Oligocene of Allier, France, but they are extremely rare. One species of the former and two of the latter are represented by a total of five bones preserved in Paris. It is clear that the mode of life, the environment and the fragility of the skeleton make it unlikely that members of the Passeriformes should be preserved as fossils. But the first fossil bird ever to be described, *Protornis glaronensis*, from the Upper Eocene of Glarus, Switzerland, is now thought to be a passerine, though its affinities are uncertain. It was described in 1839 by Hermann von Meyer and a specimen in the Zoological Museum of Zurich University has been the subject of remarkable mathematical treatment by F. Stüssi, to correct the distortions of the bones on the slab.

Further, some thousands of specimens of passerines, mainly dis-associated, have been recovered from the Rancho La Brea tar pits in the city of Los Angeles, California. This comparatively small area of tar, when covered with rain water, obviously looked like, and smelt like, a lake of fresh water and attracted many birds and mam-mals which in Pleistocene times became trapped as they stepped on to it. Since 1912 a large number of specimens from these tar pits have been brought to light, and the fauna forms one of the most outstanding features in the history of palaeontology. The birds have formed the basis of many interesting reports by Alden Miller and Dr Hildegarde Howard.

7. Origins of Ratites

Now that we have seen something of the history of the birds in the Tertiary it is possible to devote attention to the origin of the Ratites. This general term is applied to those running birds, like the emu and the ostrich, which have a breast-bone (sternum) without a keel. It has been argued by several scientists that these are primitive birds that have never flown, and as stated above (p. 24), *Archaeopteryx* (the London specimen) has been credited as being the ancestor of the Ratites whereas *Archaeornis* (the Berlin specimen of *Archaeopteryx*) was considered to be the ancestor of the Carinates.

There are several possibilities. A bird with a keel-less sternum may either be on the way to the development of a keel or may have lost it. *Archaeopteryx* may have been an ancestor of true flying birds with keeled breast-bones. On the other hand *Hesperornis*, the toothed Cretaceous diver, was certainly a form that had lost its power of flight; its breast-bone was unkeeled. There may, of course, have been birds in which a keeled breast-bone was never developed. If this supposition be granted there would be terrestrial birds that had never attained the ability to fly, but if this were so, then there would certainly be other aspects of their anatomy and physiology that would betray their terrestrial habit as clearly as the breast-bone.

The geological history of the ostriches, emus and cassowaries, as has been pointed out, is brief. The nature of the birds' environment is to blame for the absence of much older material, for as we have seen or can easily deduce from the record disclosed in the preceding pages, birds of marine or shore-living habits are by far the most usually preserved. This of itself confirms the terrestrial habits of the earlier Ratites. (Figs. 18, 24.)

Many, perhaps most, birds find their food on the ground. For them flight is of value for locomotion, for the assurance of the attainment of a safe nesting place and for escape from their enemies. But if enemies of importance are absent then the need for flight in the double sense is largely gone.

The past and present history of New Zealand and of Australia shows us that land enemies such as carnivorous mammals were

Fig. 24. The Ostrich, a typical living Ratite. About one twenty-fifth natural size. Drawn by Maurice Wilson.

absent, for the Australian marsupials can be ignored in this argument. In South America the rhea can usually see its enemies in the open country and flee, as Charles Darwin was among the first to testify in *A Journal of Researches*. The ostrich of South Africa is similarly well-endowed with speed and in the neighbouring island of Mauritius, home of the dodo, there were no carnivores.

Thus land birds living in these places were able to discard flight as of no advantage to them in their economy. This abandonment led to the adaptation of other parts of their anatomy for running. The wings tended to be less important than the legs and so the former, and their muscles and attachments, grew slighter and the leg bones became longer and stouter and their mechanisms more powerful. The tail was no longer required for flight control or correction and, as this also became less important, the underlying bony structure, the pygostyle, was lost.

This all seems quite logical and only to be expected, but there are other features which may indicate a more ancient connexion between some of the running birds. These are in the structure of the palate, where the palatal bones do not come into contact with the brain-case and where the vomers are larger than usual. These are not primitive features but show a neotenous condition in which a juvenile stage in normal development has been retained in the adult largely because of changed feeding habits consequent on loss of flight and increase in size. The cassowary, emu, ostrich, kiwi and rhea, and perhaps the tinamous of South America, must be regarded as survivors in the absence of competition, just as the Australian marsupials have lived on. The study of other groups has shown that in favourable circumstances there have always been birds ready to abandon flight and that many of these, like *Diatryma* and *Phororhacos*, became large and considerable carnivores. The remains of New Zealand moas are found either in marshy deposits, in caves, or in the kitchen middens of Maoris, and in all the countries where flightless birds, including the dodo and the solitaire, have been found, it was chiefly Man, the hunter, who directly or indirectly exterminated those that are no longer represented. (Plates 10, 11.)

The Pleistocene and late forms of New Zealand, Australia, South America, South Africa and Madagascar are united scientifically in the Superorder Palaeognathae by some authors. They are characterized by a reduced wing skeleton; a sternum with no keel; the hind legs powerfully developed; the tail with (usually) no pygostyle; no fusion of pubis and ischium distally; feathers soft and curly (another neotenous feature); palatine bones not in contact with brain-case, and vomers well developed. (See Figs. 25–28.) According to Romer's *Vertebrate Paleontology*, the superorder comprises the Orders Caenagnathiformes, Struthioniformes, Rheiformes, Casuariiformes, Aepyornithiformes, Dinornithiformes, Apterygiformes and Tinamiformes. Wetmore includes them all within the Superorder Neognathae or Typical Birds.

The conclusion must be that the Ratites are birds which, in Professor Owen's phrase, 'have abrogated the power of flight'. Their wing structure and their skeleton and the development of the cerebellum, which has certainly not been independently evolved,

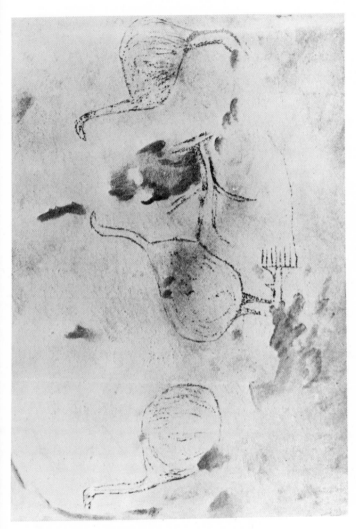

PLATE 11. Early Maori rock painting of moas at Craigmore, Pareora, South Island, New Zealand. From a copy by Theo Schoon reproduced in the New Zealand *Arts Year Book*, 1950.

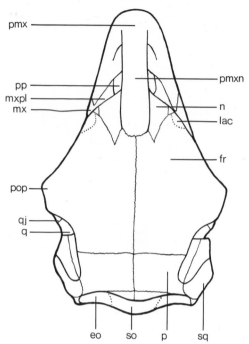

Fig. 25. Skull of a fossil moa seen from above (diagrammatic).

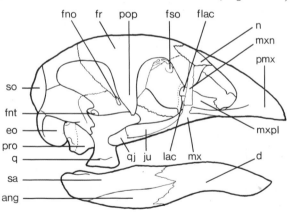

Fig. 26. Skull of a fossil moa seen from the right side (diagrammatic).

ang, angular; *ba*, basipterygoid; *bo*, basioccipital; *d*, dentary; *eo*, exoccipital; *fc*, foramen for carotid; *flac*, lacrimal foramen; *fno*, foramen for optic nerve; *fnt*, foramen for trigeminus; *fr*, frontal; *fso*, supraorbital foramen; *fv*, vagus foramen; *ju*, jugal; *lac*, lacrimal; *mx*, maxilla; *mxn*, maxillo-nasal; *mxpl*, maxillo-palatine;

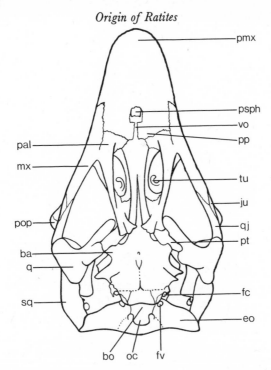

Fig. 27. Skull of a fossil moa, palatal aspect (diagrammatic).

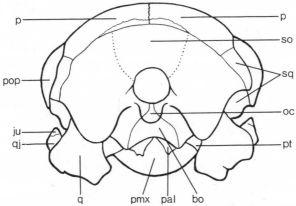

Fig. 28. Skull of a fossil moa seen from behind (diagrammatic).

n, nasal; *oc*, occipital condyle; *p*, parietal; *pal*, palatine; *pmx*, premaxilla; *pmxn*, nasal process of premaxilla; *pop*, postorbital process; *pp*, palatine process; *pro*, proötic; *psph*, parasphenoid; *pt*, pterygoid; *q*, quadrate; *qj*, quadratojugal; *sa*, surangular; *so*, supraoccipital; *sq*, squamosal; *tu*, turbinal; *vo*, vomer.

all betray their ancestry, but whether they are a natural group or merely an assemblage of forms that have each followed parallel lines of evolution is an unsolved problem.

Geological Chart

ERA	PERIOD	AGE OF BASE*	DURATION IN MILLIONS OF YEARS	CHARACTERISTIC LIFE	ASPECT OF THE EARTH
CAENOZOIC (Quaternary)	Recent		—	Man, modern birds	The Recent and Present
CAENOZOIC (Quaternary)	Pleistocene	2	2	Mammoth, mastodon, rhinoceros, sabre-tooth cat, Rancho La Brea fauna	Great glaciers covered Europe and North America, in four invasions
CAENOZOIC (Tertiary)	Pliocene	7	5	Apes and hominoids	Mountains formed and the climate cooled
CAENOZOIC (Tertiary)	Miocene	26	19	Culmination of mammal evolution	The Alps, Andes and Himalayas formed
CAENOZOIC (Tertiary)	Oligocene	38	12	Modern mammal evolution	Sea over Germany and Russia
CAENOZOIC (Tertiary)	Eocene and Palaeocene	65	27	Archaic mammals, beginning of modern birds, first penguins	Rocky Mountains formed. Sea with heavy clay deposits in S. England
MESOZOIC	Cretaceous	136	71	Flowering plants, 'toothed' birds, last dinosaurs	Marine deposits (Chalk) in England. Great inland seas in the United States. Delta deposits in S. England
MESOZOIC	Jurassic	195	59	Toothed birds and flying reptiles	Seas invaded the continents
MESOZOIC	Triassic	225	30	Dinosaurs and first mammals	Continents were high and the seas limited
PALAEOZOIC	Permian	280	55	Many land vertebrates	Northern European continent: desert areas. Glaciers in S. Africa and Australia
PALAEOZOIC	Carboniferous	345	65	Coal plants and amphibians	Extensive swamps with coal formation
PALAEOZOIC	Devonian	395	50	Land plants and many fishes	Warm, shallow seas extensive. On land, Old Red Sandstone formed
PALAEOZOIC	Silurian	440	45	Earliest land plants, giant sea scorpions and armoured fishes	Shallow, salt seas and a hot, dry climate
PALAEOZOIC	Ordovician	500	60	Cephalopods and graptolites	Invasions of sea and volcanic activity in Britain
PALAEOZOIC	Cambrian	570	70	Trilobites and brachiopods	Inland seas covered most of North America
PROTEROZOIC				Primitive forms	Ceaseless change of land and sea
ARCHAEOZOIC		4000		Earliest forms	Recurrent ice-ages, deserts and volcanic activity
AZOIC				Lifeless	Formative stage

*in millions of years

69

Classification

CLASS AVES, BIRDS

ARCHAEORNITHES (SAURIURAE)
    Archaeopterygiformes   *Archaeopteryx*

NEORNITHES
    Odontoholcae
        Hesperornithiformes   *Hesperornis, Baptornis*
    Dromaeognathidae
        Tinamiformes   Tinamous
    Ratitae
        Struthioniformes   Ostriches
        Rheiformes   Rheas
        Casuariiformes   Cassowaries, Emus
        Aepyornithiformes   Elephant Birds
        Dinornithiformes   Moas
        Apterygiformes   Kiwis
    Carinatae
        Gaviiformes   Divers (Loons)
        Podicipediformes   Grebes
        Sphenisciformes   Penguins
        Procellariiformes   Albatrosses, Petrels
        Pelecaniformes   Pelecans, Gannets
        Ciconiiformes (Ardeiformes)   Herons, Storks
        Anseriformes   Ducks, Geese, Swans
        Falconiformes (Accipitriformes)   Vultures, Hawks
        Galliformes   Pheasants, Fowls
        Gruiformes (Ralliformes)   Cranes, Rails, *Diatryma*
        Ichthyornithiformes   *Ichthyornis, Apatornis*
        Charadriiformes   Gulls, Auks, Waders
        Columbiformes   Pigeons
        Cuculiformes   Cuckoos, Roadrunners
        Psittaciformes   Parrots
        Strigiformes   Owls
        Caprimulgiformes   Goatsuckers, Nightjars
        Apodiformes   Swifts
        Trochiliformes   Humming-birds
        Coliiformes   Colies
        Trogoniformes   Trogons
        Coraciiformes   Rollers, Hornbills, Kingfishers
        Piciformes   Woodpeckers, Toucans
        Passeriformes   All the perching birds

Glossary

Acetabulum. The cup-shaped hollow or the notch in the pelvis for the head of the femur or thigh bone. In fossil birds it is usually part of the ilium, and it is usually perforate.

Ala spuria. See Bastard wing.

Allantois. A great development of the urinary bladder that grows outside the body of the embryo to lie under the outer layer of the yolk sac just inside the shell. It is richly supplied with blood-vessels and respiration takes place through these vessels in the developing bird.

Alula. See Bastard wing.

Alveolus. A pit or socket, as for a tooth; an air-cell, as in the lungs.

Amnion. The sac that encloses the unborn young is lined with the *amnion*, though the name is often given to the whole sac. The fluid (amniotic fluid) in the sac allows the young bird to develop in the egg on dry land.

Articular. One of the bones of the lower jaw and that which articulates with the quadrate above.

Articulation. The surface for the movement of one bone on another, or the movement itself.

Bastard wing. Group of three feathers attached to the first digit or 'thumb'.

Calamus. The hollow proximal part of a feather stem.

Carina. A keel; the keel for attachment of muscles on the breast-bone.

Carinates. Birds with a keeled sternum indicating flying abilities. Thus, generally, the flying birds as distinct from the Ratites (q.v.).

Carpal. One of the bones of the wrist.

Caudal. Of the tail; e.g. caudal vertebrae.

Centrum. The body or cylindrical portion of a vertebra.

Cerebellum. Part of the brain concerned with special muscular co-ordination. In birds it is a comparatively large outgrowth of the upper surface of the hinder part of the brain. (cf. Cerebrum.)

Cerebrum. The paired front parts or lobes of the upper surface of the brain. They are used in co-ordination.

Cervical. Of the neck; e.g. cervical vertebrae.

Clavicle. One of the bones of the shoulder girdle, on the front or ventral side. In man it is the collar-bone. In birds, fused with its fellow in the middle line, it forms the furcula or wishbone.

Cleidoic. 'Enclosed' egg like that of birds and reptiles in which the fluid for the embryo is contained in a more or less impermeable shell.

Cold-blooded. Characteristic of living fishes, amphibia and reptiles, in which the body temperature is not constant but varies to some extent with that of the surroundings. Reptiles acquire heat directly from their surroundings or by exertion, and lose it by radiation.

Condyle. A projection or knob of bone which moves in a depression or cup in another bone; e.g. condyle of skull which allows skull to move on the neck.

Contour feathers. The feathers which help to give the body its characteristic shape.

Convergence. The gradual approach in similarity or general appearance of two or more groups, due to the adoption of the same habits and environment and not due to relationship; e.g. fishes and ichthyosaurs; ichthyosaurs and dolphins; pterodactyls and birds.

Coracoid. One of the lower (ventral) bones of the shoulder girdle, which helps with the scapula in the formation of the glenoid cavity (q.v.).

Coverts. The short feathers which cover the body generally and also cover the quills of the remiges and rectricies. The tectrices.

Cubitals. The secondaries, a group of feathers included in the remiges.

Costal. Of the ribs.

Dentary. The tooth-bearing or toothless bone of the lower jaw.

Digit. A finger or toe. Each digit contains one or more phalanges.

Distal. Away from the body or point of attachment: e.g. distal end of the leg is at the foot. (cf. Proximal.)

Dorsal. Upper surface (back) of a crawling animal's body or backward surface of a biped. Dorsal vertebrae are those of the trunk, between the cervicals and lumbars.

Femur. The thigh bone.

Fibula. The outer and hinder bone of the two in the lower leg. See Tibia.

Foramen magnum. The opening at the back or base of the skull through which the spinal, or nerve, cord issues.

Fossa. A depression or pit.

Furcula. The wishbone or merry-thought; the distally fused clavicles.

Gait. Method or style of walking.

Gape. Amount to which the jaws can open.

Genus. One or more species (q.v.) united by characters which distinguish them from other genera; a unit of classification. With the name of the mallard, *Anas platyrhynchos*, the *whole* name is the specific name (q.v.), but *Anas* itself is the name of the genus.

Girdle. The bones constituting the shoulder and pelvic regions to ensure support of the body and attachment of the limbs are known as girdles; viz. shoulder girdle and pelvic girdle.

Glenoid cavity. The cavity or space into which the head of the humerus (or upper arm bone) fits and turns. It is composed in the birds generally of part of the scapula or adjacent parts of the scapula and coracoid.

Hallux. The great toe: hind toe of a bird.

Humerus. The upper arm bone. Connects with the glenoid fossa at its head and with radius and ulna distally.

Hyoid. The bony and cartilaginous series of bones to which the muscles of the tongue are attached and which in birds also includes part of the hearing apparatus.

Ilium. The uppermost of the three bones forming each side of the pelvic girdle. It is joined to one or more of the sacral vertebrae and usually provides part of the cup or acetabulum for the head of the femur.

Incipient. Structure showing promise of development to greater use or importance. Primitive condition of structure whose fuller development is known in later forms.

Ischium. The hinder and lower of the three bones forming each side of the pelvic girdle. It usually helps to form the acetabulum for the head of the femur.

Mandible. The lower jaw. Toothless in all known birds other than *Archaeopteryx* and *Hesperornis*.

Manus. The hand.

Maxilla. The upper jaw; toothless in all birds except *Archaeopteryx* and *Hesperornis*.

Merry-thought. The fused clavicles: the furcula. Wishbone.

Metacarpo-digitals. See Primaries.

Nares. The openings in the skull for the external nostrils.

Neopallium. Part of the roof of the brain; formed on the cerebral hemispheres. Used in general co-ordination.

Neotenous. A condition characteristic of the embryonic or juvenile stage retained by an adult, e.g. the palate of Ratites.

Neural. Neural process: the part of the vertebral structure around and above the spinal cord.

Ornithischia. One of the two great groups of dinosaurian reptiles, so-called on account of the bird-like pelvis. Related to the birds but not ancestral to them.

Patagium. The wing membrane of the flying reptiles and the bats.

Pectoral girdle. The shoulder girdle, providing attachment to the fore-limb bones and muscles and the breast-bone and muscles.

Pelvic girdle. The hip-bones, giving attachment to the hind leg bones and muscles.

Pennae. Contour feathers; includes quills and coverts.

Phalange. A bone or 'joint' in a finger or toe.

Primaries. Feathers attached to the manus; a set of the remiges; also known as metacarpo-digitals.

Proximal. Nearest to the place of attachment to the body; e.g. proximal part of arm is at shoulder. (cf. Distal.)

Pseudosuchia. An order of extinct reptiles of Triassic age, sometimes thought to have provided the ancestors of the birds.

Pubis. Forward and lower bone on each side of pelvis, directed forward, downwards and inwards to meet its fellow of the other side.

Pygostyle. The end of the vertebral column, formed by fused vertebrae which bear the rectrices.

Quadrate. Bone at the hinder end, on each side, of the upper jaw. In all reptiles articulates with the articular bone of lower jaw.

Quills. Large feathers of wing and tail. Include remiges and rectrices.

Rachis. The shaft of a feather.

Radius. The inner of the two lower arm bones.

Ratites. Birds without a keeled sternum and therefore flightless. A term mainly used for the large running birds (e.g. ostrich) of the Southern Hemisphere.

Rectrices. The tail quills or feathers.

Remiges. The wing quills or feathers.

Sacrum. Formed by the uniting of a varying number of vertebrae whose processes are attached to the ilium. It thus binds together the dorsal parts of the pelvic girdle.

Scapus. The stem of a feather.

Species. A group of similar individuals which can normally interbreed to produce fertile offspring.

Specific name A unique combination of two latinized words applied as a name to a species (q.v.); the most restricted and fundamental of the commonly used terms in biological classification. Example: *Struthio camelus*, the ostrich. In scientific literature the specific name is usually printed in italics.

Sternum. The breast-bone.

Suture. The line of junction, plain or serrated, between the bones.

Synsacrum. The last two thoracic vertebrae together with the lumbar, sacral and the first few caudals fused together.

Tarsal. Of the tarsus or ankle joint.

Tarso-metatarsus. A straight and usually strong bone formed by the fusion of the distal tarsals with the second, third and fourth metatarsals.

Taxonomy. The science of classification of animals and plants.

Tetrices. The coverts.

Tetrapod. Literally, a four-footed animal. Used scientifically to include amphibia, reptiles, birds and mammals.

Thoracic. Of the chest or thorax; thoracic ribs.

Tibia. The shin-bone; the principal bone of the lower leg.

Tibio-tarsus. One of the shin-bones formed by the fusion of the tibia with the proximal row of tarsal bones.

Ulna. One of the two lower arm bones.

Vane. The web of a feather, including barbs, barbules and rachis.

Ventral. The lower surface of an animal; or of its bones; that is, the surface nearer the ground in a quadruped and the front surface of a biped. Opposite to dorsal.

Vestigial. Remnant of a structure once of use but now disused or unimportant; e.g. pineal eye in many reptiles, vermiform appendix in man.

Vexillum. The vane of a feather.

Vomer. One of the palatal bones (Fig. 27).

Warm-blooded. The condition, as in birds and mammals, where the temperature of the body is usually constant and is not wholly dependent on the environmental conditions.

Wishbone. See Furcula.

Zygodactylous. Condition of the foot in which two of the toes are in front and two behind.

Index